David Barrah

Through My Eyes

For Ray Clarke.

Best wishes

Dave Barrah

David Barrah

Through My Eyes

The Inside Story of the 2001 Foot and Mouth Crisis

TIMEBOX PRESS

FIRST PUBLISHED IN 2005 BY

TIMEBOX PRESS

24 FOREST ROAD

BRANKSOME PARK

POOLE

DORSET BH13 6DH

TELEPHONE: +44 (0) 1202 757515

© DAVID BARRAH

© TYPOGRAPHICAL ARRANGEMENT, TIMEBOX PRESS, 2005

ISBN 0955021901

BRITISH LIBRARY CATALOGUING – IN PUBLICATION DATA.

A CATALOGUE RECORD FOR THIS BOOK IS AVAILABLE FROM THE BRITISH

LIBRARY.

TYPESET BY: TIMEBOX PRESS, POOLE

PRINTED IN GREAT BRITAIN BY ARROWSMITH, BRISTOL

COVER IMAGE: KEITH GODWIN

COVER DESIGN: KEITH GODWIN

Dedication

This book is dedicated to:-

All the farmers who suffered.

All the drivers in whose company I spent many happy hours.

The MAFF staff at Gloucester and Taunton who worked very hard under difficult and unpleasant circumstances.

All the Meat and Livestock Commission staff I worked with during my time on the Welfare Scheme, in particular Geoff Carpenter.

And most of all my long time-time friend and slaughtering companion Sam, whose sharp wit and excellent company made an unpleasant experience more congenial, and whose quick thinking probably saved me from serious injury or death on at least two occasions.

Acknowledgements

I gratefully acknowledge the assistance of many people with the production of this book. My thanks are due in particular to my wife Alison and my daughter Nicola for help with the writing of my story.

I am indebted to Anthony Gibson for kindly agreeing to write a foreword for my book. I heard his name mentioned many times during 2001 amongst the farming fraternity, even as far away as mid – Wales as being a man of high integrity and common sense. My friend Mark Thorp was full of encouragement for the project and put me in touch with Anthony Gibson.

This book had only been partly written when a chance meeting with Tim Wyatt of TimeBox Press resulted in his encouragement to complete the manuscript. Without his enthusiasm and guidance it would probably not have been published and I am very grateful to him.

Foreword

By Anthony Gibson

The outbreak of foot and mouth disease in February 2001 caught farmers, the veterinary authorities and the Government completely by surprise. Although there had been outbreaks of FMD in the Far East in the previous year, the general assumption in Britain was that this was yesterday's disease, not something that would ever pose a serious threat again. There had been no outbreak of FMD in Britain at all since 1981, when a single case on the Isle of Wight was snuffed out in a matter of days, and no serious outbreak since 1968, over 30 years previously.

That, plus the security that it is always assumed that our island status confers on us, bred what turned out to be a very false sense of security. Complacency was everywhere. There were contingency plans as to what to do in the event of a FMD outbreak, and they were rehearsed from time to time, albeit only by the MAFF vets, without involving either the farming organisations or any of the other official bodies that would have significant roles to play. But this was very much a case of going through the motions, and when it came to the real thing, the plans collapsed almost as soon as they were activated.

What made the situation far, far worse was the fact that the disease had become well established, all the way down the western half of the country, before the authorities even knew it was in the country. This meant that, instead of being able to anticipate the arrival of disease and stamp it out as soon as it appeared - as in the 1981 outbreak - MAFF was playing catch up from day one.

Nor could the disease have arrived at a worse time. For reasons connected with a now abolished subsidy regime, the early spring was the time when sheep movements were at their greatest. That, plus hopelessly inadequate movement recording, made it almost impossible to track where potentially infected consignments of animals might have gone. And just to put the tin lid on things, it turned out that this particular strain of the disease could be carried by sheep without the animals showing any obvious symptoms. So it was usually only after the infected sheep had come into contact with cattle or pigs that its presence was revealed, and by then, of course, it was too late.

I remember vividly the night the disease arrived in Devon. It was Saturday February 24th, at about 8.00 in the evening. The day before, the farmers of the South West had heaved a collective sigh of relief when the initial outbreak in Essex had been traced back to a farm in Northumberland - just about as far away from the West Country as you can get. Which made the phone call that I took from Ben Bennett, the head MAFF vet for Devon, all the more devastating:

"We've got foot and mouth in Devon", he told me, "and it's as bad as it can get."

Just how bad was soon apparent. The disease had been identified on one of many farms connected with one of the region's biggest livestock dealers, Willie Cleave, at Highampton near Hatherleigh in West Devon. The assumption had to be that if it was on one of his premises, it was probably on all of them. And so it proved. Before long, the under-prepared, under-resourced MAFF vets had a firestorm of disease on their hands, without the means even to keep it in check, let along to extinguish the flames. Once it became apparent how widespread the infection was, and how hopeless were the well-intentioned efforts to contain it, we called for the Army to be brought in to co-ordinate the slaughter and incineration arrangements and allow the MAFF vets to concentrate on tracking and diagnosing disease. But for weeks, the requests fell on deaf ears. A combination of professional pride on the part of the vets on the ground - which manifested itself in an entirely natural unwillingness to admit defeat - plus a reluctance on the part of senior Government ministers to be seen not to be coping caused a fatal delay. It wasn't until almost the end of March that Tony Blair brought the Army in and set up a command and control operation capable of co-ordinating the many different agencies, and by that time the disease was out of control.

The Government's failure to take decisive action earlier meant that the measures that were eventually taken were infinitely more draconian than would have been necessary had they not prevaricated, in the apparent hope that the disease would go away in time for a May 3 general election. The upshot was the hated contiguous cull, which led to the slaughter of tens of thousands of sheep and cattle that did not have the disease and were not even at any immediate risk of contracting it, as the mathematicians moved in with their computer models.

By the time the disease was eventually brought under control, the losses and costs had reached frightening proportions:

Over 6 million animals were killed, on 2,026 farms, at a cost to the taxpayer of over £3 billion, and probably as much again in uncompensated costs to tourism and other rural businesses.

But the figures tell not even half the story. To understand the true nature of the foot and mouth nightmare, you need to hear from the people directly caught up in it. At the time, and subsequently, we have heard a good deal from the farmers, the vets and the countryfolk who were in the front line. But what about the people who arguably had the most difficult and unpleasant task of all - the slaughtermen? Was MAFF's handling of the outbreak really as chaotic and insensitive as it appeared from the outside? And what was it like to have to go onto a farm, and destroy what to the farmer and his family might have represented a lifetime's work, or much loved family pets, especially if the animals were perfectly healthy?

David Barrah's vivid account is not for the squeamish. But it does provide a hugely valuable insight into the true nature of the 2001 foot and mouth epidemic – the biggest single disaster to befall the British countryside in modern times.

Introduction

Officially, it all began in the week beginning 19th February 2001. This was the week when the life of everybody involved in the farming meat and livestock industry in this country was turned completely upside down. It was reported that an outbreak of foot and mouth disease had been identified at an abattoir belonging to Cheale Meats in Brentwood in Essex.

Some pigs had been found to be showing symptoms of the disease. The animals concerned were some sows which had been transported from Heddon-on-the-Wall in Northumberland. The Brentwood abattoir specialises in the slaughter of sows and boars. The flesh from these animals is used entirely for manufacturing purposes (pies, sausages etc) because, by virtue of their age, it would be too tough for bacon or pork. Consequently such animals are sent from all over the country to this establishment. These particular animals had been housed in the lairage of the abattoir over the weekend awaiting slaughter on the Monday. The lairage is a holding area for the confinement of animals prior to slaughter. The stockman at the plant called the condition of the sows to the attention of the Official Veterinary Surgeon who suspected either foot and mouth or swine vesicular disease, the symptoms of both being very similar. The manager of the plant, a long-time friend of mine who worked with me as an inspector in Bristol and who had considerable experience of food animal disease, agreed with this diagnosis. All activity at the plant was suspended. Officials from the Ministry of Agriculture Fisheries and Food (MAFF) were contacted and they called in an international expert on foot and mouth disease who lives in this country. Meanwhile the affected pigs were killed to end their suffering.

Pigs in particular suffer great distress with the symptoms of this disease which include extensive ulceration on the tongue, lips and in particular the feet making it extremely painful for them to eat or walk. Cattle suffer in a similar manner. Maybe people who advocate allowing these animals to recover should consider the distress involved. Adult sheep, on the other hand, can become infected and with little obvious symptom unless closely examined, which is often not practicable, get over the acute stage of the disease. As a large part of our national flock spend at least part of their lives limping for various reasons, it is quite understandable that foot and mouth disease can be present in a flock and go entirely undetected, although very young lambs can, and do in fact, die from myocardial effects of the disease, which causes the heart muscles to malfunction. However, when infected sheep come into direct contact with pigs or cattle the presence of foot and mouth disease becomes dramatically apparent.

Whilst awaiting the expert's arrival and official diagnosis of the problem, consignments of meat already en route to their destinations in Europe were recalled to the plant as a precaution.

When the expert arrived he pronounced the sows' condition to be typical of a five-day progression of foot and mouth disease. When questioned about his certainty, observing that he may not have seen foot and mouth lesions for years, he very matter-of-factly said that he had seen it as recently as three weeks ago in Argentina. As a result of this diagnosis all animals remaining alive in the lairage of the plant and on the adjoining farmland had then to be slaughtered, an operation that went on well into the night. These, along with all carcasses already refrigerated, and everything that returned on the lorries, had to be burnt. Subsequently a rigorous cleansing and sterilising programme was undertaken followed by a long period of closure.

Although the outbreak was announced in the early part of the week, and measures were taken by the Ministry to trace the source, animal movements continued up and down the country for at least three days before measures were introduced that banned all livestock movements anywhere in the UK. Consequently all abattoirs were closed down and the farming and meat industries ground to a halt. As a result, my work as a meat inspector ceased, until a few abattoirs in unaffected areas re-opened in a limited way, slaughtering only those animals which could be transported under licence from uninfected farms. I then had some sporadic work at a couple of small plants, and at one of these experienced first hand a possible foot and mouth case. This took the form of a lip lesion on a young spring lamb, found by a young vet who was the Official Veterinary Surgeon at that particular plant. All precautionary measures were taken: the Ministry was informed, the gates of the plant closed, and the arrival of a Ministry vet was awaited. The lamb in question had been brought under licence from Devon to Somerset as one of a batch of 30. All the feet and heads of the others were retained for perusal by the Ministry vet when he arrived. He was a young man who normally worked in a practice on the South Coast who had offered his services to the Ministry. Leaving his car outside the premises he proceeded to examine in impressive detail the retained heads and feet. He then spoke to the vet who had licensed the movement from Devon, and requested that the farm of origin should be re-visited and the remaining animals, particularly cattle should be examined in detail. He also discussed the lesion with the Ministry in London. Inevitably all this took some time, and all the abattoir staff who needed sustenance had to send out and have food and drink delivered to the road gate. After much deliberation it was considered that the most likely cause of the lesion was a disease known as 'orf', a condition endemic in sheep and properly called 'contagious pustular dermatitis'. This disease is in itself a zoonosis, a disease that can be transmitted from animals to man, and is a constant problem for abattoir staff and other sheep handlers. It takes the form of lesions, particularly around the mouth and nostrils, but can also be found on occasion on the nipples and on the feet, and has often been the cause of mis-diagnosed foot and mouth outbreaks. It was well into the evening before word came from London that the restrictions on the plant could be lifted, and after disinfecting ourselves and our vehicles thoroughly, we all went home.

After this I decided that my long experience in the diagnosis of food animal disease might be of value to MAFF and I offered my services accordingly. The following chapters are a record of my experiences over the nine months that made up the 2001 foot and mouth crisis in the UK.

Chapter 1

The Fires

After offering my services to the Gloucester MAFF Office I heard nothing for some four weeks, during which time there was a fairly major outbreak of foot and mouth in and around the Severn Vale in Gloucestershire. The slaughtering staff from the plant where I had been working were employed, mostly in teams of four, to slaughter the affected stock in the area, including the hefted flocks in the Forest of Dean.

One Saturday afternoon I received a call from a good friend of mine in the Gloucester MAFF office. He asked me if I would consider working as a night fire watcher as their own staff were extremely over-stretched and they had difficulty recruiting responsible external personnel. Thinking that this might be the beginning of further more interesting work, I agreed. After a few preparations I set off to rendez-vous in the Gloucester office, there to obtain an issue of protective clothing and other items. Having visited this office some five years previously I thought I would easily find my way, but faced with three possible exits from the motorway for Gloucester I inevitably chose the wrong one. There followed a period of hyperactivity and many questions to the local population as to the whereabouts of the MAFF offices. As I knew the site extended to many acres I found it incredible that people were unaware of its existence. Desperation set in and I even tried to use my mobile phone. It had been a Christmas present from my son some three months previously. Up to this point it had remained in its box, and although I had made a couple of attempts at coming to grips with twenty-first century technology I had decided that I was happier living in the nineteenth! However I had realised that the infernal thing had its uses and as I was going to be spending periods away from home felt I should take it with me. Unfortunately my worst fears were confirmed and when it had a chance to justify its existence it let me down badly. I was unable to contact either the MAFF office or my wife at home. As time was running out I decided to abandon the office visit and go direct to the farm. I had taken the precaution of throwing a couple of clean white boiler suits and some waterproofs in the car and therefore was not completely unequipped for the night.

My earlier instruction had been to report at six pm to a farm in a village on the banks of the Severn. I had the address but was assured I would see the smoke from the fires well in advance of arrival. So assuming this would be straightforward and that it was not a very big village I set off in that direction. Driving faster than I should have been, the first incident on what should have been an uneventful trip was the double flash of a speed camera, and as mine was the only vehicle in the vicinity it was undoubtedly aimed at me. Nearing the village, and unsuccessfully scanning the horizon for smoke, I stopped to ask a young mother with a pram whether she knew the whereabouts of the farm in question. Consternation set in when her response was that she had lived in the village for some thirty years and had never heard of this farm. I stopped again outside the local hostelry and confronted a man who was just going in to enjoy his first pint of the evening. "No" he said "it's not round here". My heart sank but I thought I would try one last tack and said "Well do you know anybody who has just had foot and mouth disease confirmed?" "Oh yes" he said, "Mr Williams down the road – up here, turn right half a mile you'll be there". I thanked him profusely and set off. But my troubles were not yet over. A quarter of a mile down the road there were tapes across the road and signs saying '*Foot and mouth disease – keep out*'. As far as I could see there was no farmstead in the immediate vicinity. I got out of my car, examined the tapes and as I was debating whether to move them so I could enter, fortunately another vehicle pulled up behind me. The couple inside said "Do you <u>really</u> need to go down this road?" and I said "Well I'm from the Ministry and I need to be at this outbreak" "Follow us" they said "we live at the other side and we will take you by another route". Retracing our steps back to the main road we set off apace, and after about four miles they stopped and said "It's just up there" Thanking them for their help I drove up to the barrier which was this time right outside the farmyard. Not quite knowing what to do next I walked up to the barrier and as I did a figure in white overalls came out to greet me. This turned out to be the farmer himself and I introduced myself and indicated the reason for my being there. He told me it would be best to leave my car on the main highway and bring everything I might need with me to save returning to it. Gathering up the various bits and bobs I had brought with me I followed him towards the farm. I expressed my sorrow at his predicament, but as I also found with numerous subsequent farmers, he had adopted a philosophical attitude and accepted the inevitability of the situation.

As we turned into the farmyard the first person I saw was a good friend who is also my own veterinary surgeon. I had not even been aware that he had volunteered his services to the Ministry for the duration of the outbreak, nor he I. This was the first of several occasions when I unexpectedly met up with people I knew in another life. His first words to me were "What on earth are you doing here?" I replied "Like you, I have offered to help out and tonight I am your fire-watcher". As I said this I was reminded of Matthew Kelly and 'Stars in their eyes'.

He then said that they were a long way behind schedule and it would be some time before the fires were ready to light. The farm stock had numbered some 30 adult cattle, 20 young cattle and calves, two hundred sheep and lambs, some sows, a boar and numerous piglets and growing pigs. All these had been slaughtered earlier in the day and were awaiting transportation some quarter of a mile across fields to the pyre site. It was decided that the adult cattle should be left to be burnt the next day as daylight was fast running out and there was much work yet to do. (The fire was being built by a scratch crew under the instruction of a young lady from Agriculture Development and Advisory Service, ADAS, a MAFF agency. Although small in stature she was very much in control of the team, which numbered five or six and comprised a professional digger driver, a gamekeeper, a plasterer, an electrician and a student, who all worked very hard in the mud and adverse weather conditions.)

The design and construction of the pyre was laid down by the Ministry and commenced with the digging of a trench three feet deep and about four feet wide. The topsoil and subsoil were kept separate to facilitate re-instatement. Railway sleepers were then laid along both edges of the trench which in this instance was some forty yards long. Other sleepers were then placed across the trench at intervals and on top of these straw bales were laid three deep. Wooden pallets were then placed on top of the bales upside down and many tons of coal were tipped to cover the whole lot.

The carcasses were then carefully placed nose to tail on top. Loose straw was then sprinkled over the whole and kerosene poured on top.

It was interesting to note that even in a time of national emergency some people cannot wait to cash in. The price of sleepers had apparently doubled since the outbreak of the disease and most were being imported from France and Belgium. These sleepers had been packed into tens or dozens and strapped together and it was pointed out to me by one of the fire builders that while the outside ones appeared in good condition the inside ones were in some cases so rotten they could be crumbled in your hand.

Returning to the sequence of events, bodies were lying everywhere. The sheep had all been slaughtered in a barn and their bodies were already distended with gas to a point where they could be bounced on the ground. The smell of putrefaction was already strong after a very few hours. Sheep are particularly prone to gassing up quickly because the fleece retains the body heat for longer than is the case with other animals. This encourages the fast multiplication of the anaerobic putrefactive bacteria within the body. Sows were dead in their sties with piles of little piglets by the side of them. The Gloucester spot boar which had tried to make a run for it had eventually been cornered at the back of a large open fronted shed the floor of which was covered in liquid manure. Wishing to examine the animal more closely I started to move in its direction only to be seized by the arm by my veterinary friend who had earlier in the day found to his cost that the excrement in the shed was in places well above Wellington boot depth. Later in the evening one end of a chain was attached to the boar's leg and the other end to the hydraulic arm of a digger fully extended at a low trajectory, this being a very low roofed but deep shed. As the arm was retracted the bulk of the boar's carcase created a tidal wave of liquid manure causing the spectators to take evasive action very smartly and virtually clearing the shed in one movement!

My friend the vet asked if I would mind helping to load the carcasses. This involved pulling on ropes and the squeezing of very large stiff and bloated bodies covered in excrement through very small doorways, and then rolling them into the front bucket of a digger. He and I and the young lady from ADAS got stuck into the unpleasant task for several hours at the end of which we were plastered in excrement but were satisfied with all our endeavours. Later we were thanked by

MAFF for efforts over and above the call of duty.

Riding in one of the large vehicles I was taken for the first time to the funeral pyre site where I was to spend the night. The lighting of the pyre was a very dramatic event and was performed very efficiently by the gamekeeper in charge of the fire-building gang. With a handful of burning straw he walked smartly along the length of the fire touching the kerosene-soaked straw at intervals. Unlike petrol, which is an immediate flash, kerosene burns more slowly but once under way the whole forty yards roared into life, lighting up the night sky more dramatically than any November 5th celebration. Looking around the horizon there were two other fires I could see already burning.

All Ministry staff were now ready to leave the site and I walked with my friend back down to the farm, stumbling in the dark along very deep, water-filled wheel ruts with only the aid of a small torch. On the way we passed a large shed and adjoining compound where lay a bull and all the suckler cows which would be burnt on the morrow. My friend, who as a young man practised in Africa and there had seen outbreaks of foot and mouth disease, showed me the lesions which he had diagnosed earlier in the day. Then he and the other MAFF staff, after cleansing and disinfection, left the premises, leaving me alone on the farm with just the farmer and his wife and son.

It had been suggested to me that I should divide my time between supervising the fire and trying to ensure that the foxes or other wildlife did not avail themselves of the potential food bonanza which had suddenly been placed before them in the compound. So, slipping and sliding in the wheel ruts in the pitch dark once again, I returned to the fire. This tortuous journey was repeated many times during the night. On my return I could see two figures silhouetted in the fire glow, arm-in-arm, watching their livelihood, and in some cases animals which had become friends, being consumed by the fire.

At first I kept a distance, not wishing to intrude on their grief. They, however, drew me into conversation: the first of many similar conversations I had with the farming fraternity in this area and in Wales. The main topic was the current Government's attitude towards the smaller farmers in this country – they felt it to be at best deliberate apathy and at worst downright discrimination against those who until recently had been valued as the reliable mainstay of food production in this country. The policy now, seemed to be a total reliance on Europe and other countries for our food supplies, where standards are at best probably as good as ours but at worst are rock bottom low; the all important point being – it's cheap, never mind if it brings in a bit of foot and mouth disease. Having put the world to rights, I bade them good-night and they wished me well for the night ahead.

It was amazing how quickly some of the carcasses had been virtually consumed in the first hour, whereas others remained identifiable right through to the morning. I suppose it depended on how they were placed on the fire. There was a large stack of straw bales which were intended for the next day to burn the cattle. As there was a cold damp wind blowing, I drew up one of these bales by the fire on which to sit for warmth and consider the bizarre situation in which I found myself. I think there is a fascination with fire somewhere deep in the human soul which is very primeval in origin and I felt this very strongly with this particular fire – probably the largest bonfire I have ever seen, being as I was totally alone in an unknown environment, completely enveloped by darkness. It was not however a silent vigil as I could hear the hissing of the burning fat, the muffled explosions of bursting stomachs and the showers of sparks as occasional carcasses became unstable and rolled off the fire. At first I tried to return them to the flames with the aid of a pitchfork but the incredible heat drove me back. It was interesting to see the effect of this searing heat on the carcasses as the front legs were drawn up to the body as the tendons contracted.

Now I considered the wider noises of the night, my attention first being drawn to the screaming of a vixen only a few hundred yards away; an eerie cry under any circumstance but in this situation particularly so. I tried to pick up her eyes with the torch but she must have been on the other side of the hedge. As most fox courtship is done in January and early February, and the date was March 24th, this was somewhat late and her cries went unanswered by a dog fox and eventually ceased as she moved away into the distance.

As I have already mentioned my exact location and surroundings were unknown to me but listening to the calls of curlew and lapwing and the quacking of mallard I realised I could not be far from the Severn Estuary. Surprisingly, several times during the night I could hear the bleating of sheep not very far away and thought that probably, as this was a confirmed outbreak, that they would not have long to live.

After a while a cold wind sprang up preceding a heavy rain shower. With no other shelter in the field, and that afforded by the farm buildings being a quarter of a mile of slipping and sliding in deep ruts away, I built myself a speedy shelter out of bales, a tiny sanctuary whence I would repair on several occasions during the night.

Returning to the fire, after one of my numerous trips back and forth, as dawn was breaking I was able to see for the first time the perimeter hedges of the fire field. As the light improved I could see a human form, together with a dog, peering through the hedge at the fire. I felt duty bound to go over and enquire as to the necessity for his presence so close to the fire. It appeared that he was the owner of the sheep I had heard during the night and his land, on which he kept 600 ewes, encircled the fire field. He had already been told that his sheep would have to die in contiguous slaughter, it was just a question of when. During the course of the conversation it emerged that he was a part-time slaughterman, as well as a farmer, and he was wondering whether he would be called upon to slaughter his own sheep. Whether he ever did or not, I shall never know. I wished him well for the future, and he took his leave.

Daylight was now coming on apace and I knew it would not be long before the farmer and all the Ministry staff returned. By now the fire had consumed the vast majority of the bodies and large areas had collapsed down in into the pit beneath. Even though the heat was still incredible I was able, with the aid of the pitchfork, to return the charred bodies which had fallen off during the night, to the fire. It was interesting to note that, even though the fire had been evenly laid, there were areas along the length where individual animals, which I had come to recognise during the night, remained identifiable, although obviously badly charred. Whilst engaged in my stoking activities the farmer returned and we chatted at length about the terrible plague that had befallen the countryside in particular, and the parlous state of agriculture in general. I was unsure of the exact hour as I never wear a wrist watch, but I remembered that it was the weekend when the clocks went back. This had obviously confused the Ministry team as to the time of their arrival, as they drifted back in ones and twos. The gamekeeper foreman, thanked me for my efforts with the fire, but commented that it would all have been done much quicker with the digger bucket as was apparently their normal habit. I left them as they prepared to go through the whole process again to burn the cattle carcasses. I trudged down the muddy track for the last time and after being pressure-washed and disinfected by the lady from A.D.A.S, I returned to the car.

Once a person had visited a farm where animals had foot and mouth (or a farm contiguous to a farm with foot and mouth), they became 'dirty' and could not visit a 'clean' farm for at least three days but preferably seven days. Being now classified as "dirty", I was unable to return to my home because we keep a few sheep. I had taken the precaution of renting a room in a friend's house in Clevedon. I remained there in anticipation of my next job, if indeed there was going to be a next job, but also becoming 'cleaner' by the minute and being 'clean' would allow me to return home to my own animals. I was eventually contacted on the Monday and asked to attend a fire that night, in the middle of the Forest of Dean. Meanwhile my veterinary friend had supplied me with some Ministry issue overalls and waterproofs from the stores in Gloucester.

Setting off, having allowed plenty of time for a 6pm arrival, I inadvertently took the wrong road and ended up crossing the Severn on the new bridge, instead of the old one as I had planned. This meant a long and time wasting drive on the Welsh side of the river, using up all the spare time I had allowed to locate the farm. As I passed through the village of Blakeney I was surprised to see a fire being prepared virtually in the middle of the village. On consideration, I concluded that occasionally it must be impossible to move stock away from proximity to human habitation. However, later in the epidemic it would appear to be perfectly acceptable to transport potentially infected stock over great distances, either to be rendered, incinerated or buried.

I continued on to the village of Newnham and turned left into the Forest, needing to ask directions from only one local person. I followed a tiny little lane for about a mile to the farm. This time I could follow the smoke, as incineration was already in progress. Parking my car some distance from the fire I proceeded on foot to meet Peter, a young man from A.D.A.S who was in charge of the disposal team. He took me into the farmhouse to meet the farmer and his wife and son. As I was to find so many times over the next few months, they were extremely generous in their hospitality despite their personal anguish and predicament. Tea and cake was immediately offered and the inevitable topics of conversation ensued whilst the food and drink was consumed. Peter, eager to complete his day's work, was anxious to return to his team, who were engaged in pressure-cleaning the lane. I will return to the dubious merits of so called bio-security in a later chapter.

I climbed the slight slope behind the farm to inspect the fire, which had been built in a line some 50 yards long running up the hill. Again a very professional job had been done of separating topsoil and subsoil. The stock concerned consisted of ewes and lambs and some 50 head of young beef cattle. The view out over the Severn Estuary was panoramic, looking across the U-bend in the river to a village I now know to be Arlingham, which will appear again later. Having washed the road, the MAFF staff went their various ways, an interesting fact given that the farmer was to tell me he had been confined to the holding and had to send out for supplies.

My lonely vigil began as daylight departed. Taking now closer stock of my surroundings I could see I was in the centre of a cluster of dwellings, tucked secretly away behind trees and folds in the ground. The lane obviously gave access to many of these and there was quite a lot of traffic coming and going during the evening and the following morning with much slowing and stopping to view the fire. Huge skeins of herring gulls passed overhead heading downriver to their homes on Flatholm, Steepholm and the little Denny Island further down the channel. The night closed in, and the photography started. Sightseers arrived on an adjacent hill and until well after midnight the darkness was punctuated by flashbulbs. Fire photography had obviously become a local pastime. As the carcasses were consumed and parts of the fire started to collapse, the strong wind, which had sprung up during the evening carried spectacular showers of sparks high up into the night sky. As I walked my circuit around the fire many times during the night I wondered how often my silhouette had been captured to later appear in photograph albums, even though the photographer and the subject had never met.

As the night wore on the lights in the surrounding properties went out one after the other and, eventually, apart from the fire and the odd camera flash on the adjacent hill, the night became very dark. Inevitably the first of several heavy showers started. On this occasion there were no convenient straw bales to make a shelter, so I retreated to the nearest farm building. This was of corrugated iron construction, and was stacked solid with farm machinery, fence posts and various other bric-a-brac, allowing absolutely nowhere to sit. Seeking somewhere more comfortable, I moved towards a much larger barn, but my approach was heralded by deep growls from within. Discretion being the better part of valour, and not wishing to start a barking session, I retraced my steps to the first shed and stood uncomfortably listening to the rain on the iron roof. During the clear periods of the night, and whilst walking the length of the fire, I could see in the light of the fire one place where the excavations had revealed a narrow band of pottery shards. Obviously this area had been used at one time for disposal of household waste from the old farmhouse, long since grassed over and forgotten. Being interested in things archaeological, my mind turned to 'Time Team', and what they would have made of these little pieces of pottery from long ago, thought to have been buried forever, but unexpectedly exposed by the foot and mouth epidemic.

The night dragged on uneventfully, interspersed only by heavy showers, but as the day began to break the surrounding woods, fields and gardens exploded into the best dawn chorus of birdsong I have heard since I was a child. Blackbirds, song thrushes, mistle thrushes, wrens, dunnocks, robins, and in the background a woodpecker drumming on a dead branch, all declared their ownership of their various territories. A carrion crow landed on an adjacent telegraph pole assessing the likelihood of a potential meal, but when he suddenly saw me he beat a hasty retreat.

Whilst once again sheltering in my shed, I reviewed my immediate surroundings in the daylight. Alongside my refuge ran the track used on the previous day by the heavy machinery digging the pyre trench and ferrying out the bodies. Consequently with constant rain this had been churned to a slurry. On the other side of this track, by a pile of old fencing stakes and a jumble of sheep wire, a movement caught my eye. Focussing on it I could see the head and shoulders of a large brown rat who had probably been scavenging fragments of blood and tissue from the recent slaughter. It became obvious that this offensive rodent wanted to return to its nest across the track and into the shed where I was sheltering. Having spent all my life observing animals I know that if the human outline is indistinct from its background and remains motionless and the wind is not carrying your scent to the animal it will continue with its normal behaviour. This applies from the red deer right down to mice. On this occasion the rat sensing no danger, picked its way carefully across the slurry directly towards me. Waiting until it was about a yard from me. I jumped in its direction, causing it to flee blindly back the way it had come, losing its sense of direction as it tried to fight its way through a tangle of sheep wire. It found sanctuary only a split second before my boot descended where it had been a moment before.

The early risers in the surrounding houses set out for work and it was not long after I had tidied the fire for last time that Peter returned and the hustle and bustle of the day began. Taking my leave and returning down the narrow winding lane, I considered the difficulties which must have been encountered by the drivers delivering large quantities of coal, pallets and straw to these out of the way farmsteads, a problem with which I was to have direct involvement later on. Driving down the main road alongside the Severn Estuary towards Chepstow and the bridges I was suddenly confronted by a roadblock. The local constabulary were redirecting traffic to avoid passing slaughter taking place at yet another outbreak.

My particular circumstance of not being able to return home until I became 'clean' made the sporadic nature of fire-watching impractical for me to continue. Shortly after my decision to curtail this activity government policy changed, due to the concerns of people living in the vicinity as to the toxic effect of the hazardous chemicals deposited in the environment. Henceforth the fires ceased and the carcasses were either burnt in incineration plants, rendered in rendering plants, or buried in specific new sites or in designated landfill sites. It is interesting to note that in some places where sufficient research had not been done as to the water table, sheep carcasses had to be disinterred and re-interred elsewhere. Also, at a later date where bovine animals had been cremated on pyres it was deemed necessary to dig up the ashes for fear of any possible BSE contamination and take them elsewhere.

Chapter 2

The learning curve

A few days later I heard on the grapevine that several teams of professional slaughtermen had returned from the killing fields in Gloucestershire to their base plant, which had been redesignated as a killing point rather than a licensed abattoir. This change of status was in order to implement the new Government scheme which went under the interesting name of the Farm Animal Welfare Scheme of which I will detail much more later.

I surmised that this might mean that the Ministry would be short of skilled licensed personnel in the locality and phoned a good friend and fellow casual meat inspector, Sam, who I knew was, like myself, a long-term licensed slaughterman. He expressed his interest in pooling our resources and once again approaching the Ministry to see if there was slaughtering work available. He rang MAFF in Gloucester and they enquired whether we had our own slaughtering weapons. When told that we could acquire these they expressed interest as it would seem that the Ministry weaponry was in short supply. Thanking them we awaited developments.

Surprisingly we were contacted later that same day and asked if we could do a job that same evening. This job was located near the village of Aust, which as some of my older readers may recall, is where the ferry boats used to cross the Severn to Chepstow in the days before the first Severn Bridge was built. Unfortunately we were not able to ready ourselves in time, having been taken by surprise at the speed at which our services were requested. However, I deduced from the location of the outbreak and the number of ewes and lambs involved that the farm concerned probably belonged to a childhood friend of mine. I later decided to ring him to commiserate with him should these be his animals. My fears were confirmed, and as we spoke shots could be heard in adjoining farm buildings as those who eventually had been chosen to conduct the slaughter went about their business. My friend, as I subsequently saw with so many people, was completely shell-shocked by the speed at which events had overtaken him. From visible diagnosis of lesions on one lamb to the destruction of his entire flock and way of life had taken only a few hours.

This is, of course, how the slaughter policy should be conducted: speed of slaughter is essential. Sadly, when in the grip of a tidal wave of disease, one often cannot wait for blood test confirmation and no blame should be attached to veterinary surgeons who inevitably at such a time are going to make occasional mistakes where other diseases and conditions which closely resemble foot and mouth disease are encountered. Conversely, if a contiguous slaughter is not carried out following a confirmed outbreak, there is a strong possibility that pockets of infection in its early stages may be missed and this will allow the disease to gain time and a stronger foothold.

Once blood samples were analysed, my friend's apparent outbreak turned out to be a false alarm, but the cleaning and disinfection of his farm buildings had gone on apace. However, as soon as the negative report was received all personnel and cleansing equipment were withdrawn.

Returning to the main theme of my story, we let it be known that we would be ready for work from the following morning. Our instruction then was to call in to the MAFF offices in Gloucester to be issued with necessary equipment by way of waterproofs suits, disposable one-piece overalls, ordnance survey maps, sachets of disinfectant, buckets, brushes, gloves and bundles of disposable pithing canes for use with the captive bolt pistol. Whilst in these offices I was able to chat to several old friends in the Ministry and put faces to the voices we had been in contact with over the phone. We also met yet another casual meat inspector from Wales who was signing on to supervise the building of funeral pyres which were still being used at this time. The whole department was buzzing with activity and my impression was of very long working hours and a grim determination to succeed in what was becoming an unpleasant and almost overwhelming situation.

Our first job allocation was made and this was to be the slaughter of 50 sheep at Newent in Gloucestershire. This was also probably as far as the Ministry was concerned a test to make sure we were fully competent. The directions we were given to the farm were inadequate, but eventually we found ourselves amongst little clusters of holdings with only one track leading to several properties. When we finally arrived we could see an Army vehicle and a car waiting for us on the side of the road. The young lady vet, whose face appeared familiar to me at a distance, suddenly looked at me and said "Oh hello Dave, what are you doing here?" Then I realised that she had been a veterinary student who had spent time with me learning practical meat inspection skills some three or four years previously. Accompanying her was a young student vet from Glasgow Veterinary College; the first of quite a few students we met during our activities. The Army personnel consisted of a young man and a young woman both of whom looked rather as if they wished they were not there: the young woman in particular hardly spoke two words and spent nearly the entire time at the farm sitting in the army vehicle.

We chatted with the farmer whilst his wife made everybody a cup of tea. It appeared that only five of the sheep were his property and were of extremely high pedigree and value, with long flowing grey wool. The remaining 45 sheep were commercial ewe lambs from the previous year some of which were pregnant, and were intended for future breeding stock. Their owner rented the grazing from this farmer as he did in several other places. Unfortunately on one of his other holdings there had been a confirmed outbreak, and as he had visited all his sheep all his stock was at risk. This was the reason that these animals had to be slaughtered. The owner of the majority of the sheep had rounded them up with the dog and penned 47 of them in a rather insecure corral composed on three sides of sheep hurdles and on one side of some fairly floppy sheep wire. In retrospect, we should not have accepted this less than secure arrangement, especially as the remaining three ewes had been confined in a very secure cattle holding pen made out of half railway sleepers and telegraph poles which was probably strong enough to have restrained an elephant. The man with the dog then departed, not wishing to be present at the slaughter. Again, on reflection, to let him leave with his dog was probably not very wise, in case we had any escapees. This also raises another issue which we encountered many times – one cannot sterilise a dog! But in many circumstances it is impossible to round up sheep without one. During the course of our endeavours we had the pleasure of watching many brilliant collie dogs working – some of them sadly for the last time. Although it never happened to us, we did hear of slaughtermen being asked to destroy the dogs together with the sheep. Some others, as we read in the newspapers, were dumped by unscrupulous farmers and ended up in animal shelters and dogs' homes. Considering the rapport which can be seen between a farmer and his working dog, it is hard to imagine how anyone could discard such a faithful companion in such a callous manner. (Hopefully however the vast majority were kept by their owners in anticipation of re-stocking or just as pets).

Turning back to the job in hand, I asked the young vet how she would like to us to go about the slaughter, by which I meant what sort of weaponry did she want us to use. She said she had only ever seen a captive bolt pistol being used, but was very interested to see the efficiency of a .22. From experience when slaughtering sheep I find a short round to be more than adequate for the job. It also has the advantage that it does not exit the head of an adult sheep, but for the sake of safety I always shoot from above towards the ground. When slaughtering young lambs it is best to shoot an adult sheep first and then to hold the lambs over the dead body while they are shot so that the bullet is absorbed in the carcase beneath. I should point out that I am one of the few people still licensed to keep a .22 pistol. A license granted to me for the humane destruction of animals and used when I am called by the Police usually after an animal is injured in a road traffic accident.

It was decided that I would demonstrate the .22 on the three sheep in the strong compound and as I could stand above them and look down it took only seconds to drop all three. Impressed by the speed, efficiency and humanity of this method of killing the vet invited me to continue the slaughter of the remaining animals in a like manner.

Standing in a line in the flimsy pen together with my friend, the vet and the vet student to try and keep the sheep away from the least secure side, I began to systematically shoot the remaining sheep. The young Army man had taken up a position outside the pen and explained to us that he was not allowed to assist our efforts with the animals. By this time there was no sign of the young woman who, no doubt, had retired to the Army vehicle. One could not help but wonder what their purpose there was. In fact, had they been actively helping, a couple of extra pairs of hands might have prevented what was about to happen.

I was down to the last five sheep when they decided to rush our defensive line which could not be stretched any further with only four people. Three of the five jumped clean over the flimsy perimeter of sheep wire. We were now in something of a predicament as the three fugitives watched us warily from a hundred yards away. I quickly shot the remaining two whilst we considered what to do next. Those of you who have ever tried to round up three sheep in a ten acre field without the assistance of a dog will appreciate that the task ahead of us was indeed daunting. Turning to Sam, who is a very experienced deer stalker, I said "Can you cleanly kill those sheep from this distance with your big bore deer rifle?" "Yes" he said "I could". I said "I think then that is the only option left open to us".

For something like this to happen was the very last thing we needed, bearing in mind this was our first job and something of a test situation. However this had all arisen because of inadequate fencing on the part of the departed owner, and the total lack of co-operation from the Army staff in assisting us with the containment of the sheep.

Sam had to return to the car, to collect the deer rifle, cleansing himself on the way, all of which would take some time. The vet and I decided to try just once, with the aid of the student, to quietly walk the sheep around the perimeter of the field with a view to walking them back into the compound. To our surprise and relief they returned to their dead comrades; the last thing in the world I thought they would do. Sadly, having got a taste for jumping fences, one of them jumped out on the far side into an adjoining field. This was potentially an even worse scenario because we did not know at that stage whether that land belonged to the same farmer or somebody entirely new. Something had too be done and done quickly. The single sheep remained at about a 30 yard distance. I knew that this was only because of the presence of the two live sheep now confined in the compound and that if they were killed first the other one might well run off, potentially contaminating another farm. The vet asked whether I could kill the one sheep at that distance. I hesitated, knowing the limited capabilities of a .22 shot round and open-sighted rifle without anything to rest on. Time was of the essence because at any moment the sheep could have bolted prior to Sam's return with a big bore rifle. Having been a reasonably good rifle shot all my life I thought that under the circumstances the risk must be taken. With a short prayer I lined up on a frontal shot and was very satisfied to see the sheep collapse in a pile. The possibility of wounding did not bear thinking about. By the time Sam returned the job was complete and we could relax.

After a final check around the bodies, and waiting for the vet and the student vet to complete their examination, we returned to the car, noticing as we passed over the grassland quantities of rabbit droppings, these being of interest to shooting people such as us. As we neared the farmhouse the farmer came out to meet us, surprisingly with a smile on his face. Unbeknown to us, he had witnessed the whole sorry episode from his kitchen window. Turning to me he said "That was some shot! Can you come back another time?" Bemused by his question I enquired why? "To shoot some of these bloody rabbits!" he said. This was the first of many amusing little incidents in what was otherwise a very tragic and sad situation. The farmer assured us that the ground onto which the runaway sheep had jumped was all part of his holding, so all was well that ended well. He thanked us for our efforts and we washed and disinfected ourselves before taking our leave, discarding our disposable overalls which would be collected with dead sheep.

Chapter 3

The Numbers Increase

The next day we progressed further into the large number of animals to be slaughtered and our task was to dispatch 1,000 ewes and lambs in the middle of the Forest of Dean. There was, however, a possible complication in that we were told that the Army were training some young men to slaughter so that they could be deployed in Cumbria where the disease raged on and thousands of animals awaited slaughter. We were told that we need not be involved in the training as the Army would be supplying its own instructors but that we should proceed with our work in the normal way.

Arriving on the site at about 8 o'clock we found that the preparations for our work to begin were nothing like complete. The sheep were still out at grass and they could be seen over many fields stretching away into the distance, all busily grazing, totally unaware of their impending fate. As if the sight of white blobs as far as one could see was not a sufficiently daunting prospect, we were told there were more belonging to the same owner some three miles away. Matthew, the young vet who greeted us, had a student in tow and they seemed to have everything under control. They told us that a man with two dogs was soon to arrive to start rounding up the sheep in batches. We volunteered to help construct the necessary pens and races out of sheep hurdles which had just arrived from a hire firm on a flat bed lorry driven by a very pleasant young student who told us that his instruction was not to come onto the ground but to leave the hurdles on the side of the road. Forming a chain with some of the Army lads we passed the hurdles along through a stone-walled compound which led in turn into a stone-built barn and thence to the open fields. Interestingly, in the corner of this compound were two beehives. As those present seemed to have little or no knowledge of bees and their habits, I thought a few words of caution would not go amiss. Having kept bees myself in the past I realised that, even though it was still early in the year, as the morning progressed and the day began to warm up the bees would become active and any moving presence in the flight line to their hives could trigger an attack. If that happened the ensuing vast numbers of angry bees would not allow any work to be done in that area for the rest of the day. I therefore suggested that before we did anything else we should cordon off a large area around the hives with sheep hurdles.

The plan then was to round up the sheep in batches, drive them from the fields through the barn into the compound and then draw a few at a time back into the barn for slaughter. Additionally, we erected some pens adjoining the barn on the field side which would contain some sheep for the young Army lads to practise on. This was hardly the best circumstance for these young men to learn what is a skilled occupation because, due to the horrendous weather which had recently prevailed, it did not take very long for these restraining pens to become a quagmire of mud. The two instructors had come from an Army abattoir in Aldershot which, as I understand it, teaches young men how to procure and dress food animals while on active service in far-flung corners of the globe. They were men of the highest possible calibre and professionalism.

During the building of these pens and races we were under the instruction of the shepherd who had now arrived with his dogs. One of his skills was the ability to assess at a glance what would be necessary for a round up of this magnitude. He taught us how to strengthen a line of hurdles by what is known as 'spragging', a local term, which involves erecting at intervals a hurdle placed at right angles to the run of the rest. This simple procedure stood us in good stead on many occasions in the future, and the frequent use of this term between Sam and I gave us the undeserved appearance of experts!

We made a quick check on the bees who, as the sun rose, were coming out to sit on their landing stage humming quietly and assessing their new horizons prior to setting off on their labours of the day. All was now ready and the collie dogs, who until now had been sitting in the back of a van in anticipation of their days work, were now released and sent to collect in the sheep from the first field. In so doing they produced a delightful display of synchronised dog work, the first of many such displays I would witness over the ensuing months.

The forward planning paid off well and, whilst the sheep were being gathered, several large bulker lorries were backed into the field ready to remove the resultant carcasses and take them to landfill sites. Running small batches into the barn the slaughter began amidst a cacophony of sheep noise where mothers had become separated from their offspring and were desperately trying to call them back. This was the first occasion when we killed ewes with their small lambs, a very distressing experience and sadly something which was to become commonplace.

The killing proceeded well enough and was in part witnessed by two representatives from the Welfare of Farm Animals at Slaughter Group, their presence probably due in part to the training of the young squaddies being carried out at this particular venue. We had filled one bulker lorry when I noticed, whilst driving in yet another batch, one very young lamb which was obviously extremely unwell and was being buffeted and in danger of being tramped by the surrounding sheep. To save it further suffering, I bent down and picked it up and carried it into the barn where I shot it and then passed the body to Matthew, the vet, who on close examination found some suspicious lesions in its mouth. These, coupled with possible heart problems as described earlier, probably accounted for the sorry condition of this little animal. The finding of lesions on this and several other animals dramatically changed the situation on this farm. What had been a contiguous cull became a potential further outbreak. This meant that the carcasses could no longer be removed from the site and necessitated the first lorry to return (with great difficulty due to the mud) to the field and unceremoniously tip out its sorry cargo in a pile. Also slaughter halted temporarily while the new situation was discussed with the Gloucester office and Head Office in London.

Having killed the vast majority of animals on the primary site it was suggested by the vet that he remained on this site whilst the Army completed the job and Sam and I, together with the shepherd and his dogs and the vet student, moved onto the second site some two or three miles away to kill about 150 sheep. Two Ministry Field Officers also came with us. Their job in normal times was the trapping and killing of badgers in areas suspected of being contaminated with bovine tuberculosis, yet another cattle plague, which is increasing with alarming rapidity in certain areas of the country. Because this serious bacterial infection takes much longer to manifest itself than the rampant viral infection of foot and mouth disease it does not attract the publicity that I think it should, and I predict that this could potentially be a far more catastrophic event for the farming community than foot and mouth. The Field Officers were to assist us with the assembly of any hurdle pens that might be needed in what turned out to be a farmyard and barn complex surrounded by very undulating and pitted ground. The pits had evidently been small defunct quarry workings going back to the days when small quarries were excavated to obtain stone for maybe one or two dwellings. The area was obviously one of good quality substrata stone because in the distance could be seen the fresh diggings of a modern quarry complex.

The sheep in question were in an area of some 30 or 40 acres but, by virtue of the undulations of the ground, had managed to secrete themselves throughout this enclosure. As it was obviously imperative that every last one was accounted for the dogs had their work cut out achieving this end. The gathering area was composed of a yard with semi-derelict barn buildings surrounding it; a site for which, were it to become available, a developer would give his right arm. We corralled the sheep in several pens in one corner of this yard and began our work.

It was not long before the veterinary student, a very competent young lady, started to find lesions in these sheep as well. Whether these and the ones we killed earlier in the day were ever confirmed with the disease I shall never know, but assuming that they were it would be interesting to know how transmission had occurred over some three miles, be it on the wind or by some other means. Her findings were reported to Matthew by mobile phone whilst we completed our task. We then returned to the original site for final pressure-clean and disinfection. As we took our leave we could see a small hill of dead sheep and lambs awaiting the construction of yet another funeral pyre and when passing the site a couple of days later on our way to a further job we could see quite a pile of dead cattle which must have been brought from elsewhere, obviously all to be burnt in the one field.

Chapter 4

The Jobs Came Rolling In

The following day our work allocation moved to a different area and we headed for north Gloucestershire. The first of three jobs for the day was to kill 150 sheep located at four different sites all belonging to the same owner. The vast majority, confined in a modern barn, were ewes and lambs; in another location were a few of last years lambs; in another field were the stock rams; and by the farmhouse a few very recently lambed ewes with their lambs. Our overall impression was of a small, well-managed sheep unit, and when we arrived all was ready for us to make a start.

We dealt with the smaller batches first. As these were a mile or so apart this necessitated the changing of our disposable overalls at each site. We finally arrived at the barn, where time was taken to separate the lambs from the ewes for the reasons already described. It was then decided by the vet that the instruction from MAFF to kill all the small lambs by barbiturate should be strictly adhered to and I would agree that, when the alternative is to shoot them with a captive bolt pistol, this probably is the best way. However, whereas the captive bolt is a heavy and ungainly weapon and could be said sometimes to be difficult to apply to a tiny lamb's head, my very light-weight free bullet pistol with its long barrel was the ideal weapon to instantly dispatch any category of sheep from the tiniest to the largest. In fact, on a good many occasions in our later work, the vets expressed their complete satisfaction with our methods. Nevertheless, on this occasion, even though I explained the difference between my pistol and the captive bolt pistol, which was probably all they had hitherto seen, the vet and the vet students persisted with injecting these little lambs through the chest wall into the heart. Unfortunately, in several instances this procedure failed to effect an instantaneous result and the lambs concerned were staggering around bleating. This meant that, whilst engaged in slaughtering the larger lambs, I had to reach out and grab these poor little creatures and shoot them anyway. I would hasten to add that on other occasions where the injection procedure was carried out, it was done in a most professional manner, but I question why it was necessary when a proven better method was available and actively endorsed by the more perceptive vets we later worked with. However, the job was completed satisfactorily and we took our leave after the usual disinfection.

As we began our journey to our next location I pointed out to Sam that the surrounding fields were very familiar to me even though we were 60 miles from home. This was because I had been there shooting woodpigeons on a partially flooded field of maize only two months earlier with a gamekeeper friend. On that visit we had seen that the field had been flooded to a much greater depth as evidenced by a tide-line on the surrounding hawthorn trees some eight feet off the ground. Indeed, there had been a drowned sheep tangled high up in a thorn bush amongst other debris left behind by the waters. The maize in the field had not been harvested because of the wet conditions and what had been a disastrous crop for the farmer had become a food bonanza for about a thousand woodpigeons which in turn had provided us with some good sport.

Another job, another place, another vet – this time a lady vet who, once we had described our methods, allowed us to proceed with the task of slaughtering 50-odd ewes and their lambs which were already penned and awaiting our arrival. In the middle distance we could see the sheep on an adjoining property being rounded up with quad bikes, and before we had finished our job someone from there came to borrow some ammunition for a captive bolt pistol which we were able to supply. It was indeed fortunate for them that we were in the vicinity.

The third job of the day, which was within walking distance, was the slaughter of only about 20 sheep. These particular animals were semi-pets and belonged to a group of householders who had evidently purchased a paddock at the rear of their properties, presumably to save it from development. The ewes were of Suffolk type and looked fairly pure bred. Running with them was the biggest Suffolk ram I have ever seen in my life, bearing in mind that I once worked at an abattoir which specialised in killing ewes and rams, and on a regular basis would kill a thousand stock rams a week. This will give you some idea of the size of this individual.

Entering the field we found a permanent sheep handling compound with a race, well constructed, which we knew would facilitate our work. The gentleman who came to greet us, the owner of one of the houses, was obviously the main custodian of the sheep and when we offered to help to round them up he said there would be no need as he had bucket of feed with him, and all that was required was a rattle of the bucket and the ewes, ram and lambs would come running, which in fact proved to be the case. Their owner put a few sheep nuts into a trough in the pen and without a backward glance the sheep went in to consume them. I could see that their owner was distressed and suggested that perhaps he might like to leave. He said, however, that he was used to taking lambs to the abattoir to be killed for home consumption, but I felt that witnessing the destruction of his breeding stock virtually in his back garden would be an entirely different experience. Nevertheless, he bravely elected to stay. Knowing that they can be unpredictable I decided to kill the ram first. Ram's heads, even without horns, can very resistant to shot, so on this occasion I selected the captive bolt pistol with a heavy cattle charge in it. This weapon is perfectly capable of stunning large bulls so I thought it to be the best option for a ram of these gigantic proportions. I entered the enclosure and it was immediately evident that this large animal had had enough of these white-clad visitors who could possibly be a threat to his ewes and I could see by the wild look in his eyes that his intention was eject me from his territory. He took two or three steps backwards, which is always the precursor to a charge, and then launched his attack at an incredible speed for such a large animal. Had it not been for my long experience of such behaviour in sheep he could easily have caught me off guard and inflicted grievous injury, particularly had he managed to squash me against the perimeter fence. Side-stepping his charge, and using all my insignificant weight to hold him against the fence I shot him, with a feeling of great sorrow at having destroyed such a magnificent and spirited beast. I have learnt to be particularly wary of rams and their capabilities, having had my ribs broken several years ago by my own Wiltshire Horn ram who had stealthily crept up unobserved and hit me in the chest just for the hell of it while I was crouching down concentrating on something else. Seriously though, had he caught me in the head he might well have killed me.

But I digress. We swiftly accounted for the ewes and lambs. By now the owner was severely traumatised. We were then told that there was one baby pet lamb remaining. He had been living, between his bottle feeds, in a large chicken run close to the house. When called he happily came skipping up to us and followed us into the killing pen totally unafraid. Young lambs love to play "king of the castle" when they have something to jump up on and this one was no exception. He jumped onto the body of his dead father and it was there that I shot him.

Chapter 5

Friday 13th

On Good Friday, Friday 13th April we were assigned a job on a farm back in the Forest of Dean. It was not the biggest job we undertook but it was a fairly emotive and notable one. My partner Sam and I had already done some work in the immediate vicinity. This farmer had two hundred plus cattle of various ages from week old calves through to the matriarchs of the herd. They were to be part of the contiguous slaughter, and we had been given the job to carry this out. We arrived mid-morning, driving down a lane to find a lovely old farmhouse with a large lake in front set in a delightful and tranquil valley. What idyllic surroundings but what a tragedy was about to unfold!

The veterinary surgeon came to greet us as we arrived. We were to work with Robert on this and subsequent occasions and found him to be a pleasant man and thoroughly practical and professional in his approach. On this occasion we had been asked by the Gloucester MAFF office, to look after Robert as he was new to the foot and mouth experience, and it was thought that we, being old hands having done at least two jobs, could show him the ropes. Robert was not a MAFF vet, but was one amongst many who had offered their services to try and bring the tidal wave of this disease under control. Vast numbers of professional staff were required because once having diagnosed foot and mouth disease on a farm they became technically "dirty" and could not visit another "clean" farm for at least three, and preferably seven, days. The virus has been known to live in the mucous lining of a humans nose and throat, particularly the tonsils, for up to three days and in that time could be transmitted to susceptible quadrupeds. Problems inevitably arose because of the delay between suspicion and confirmation of diagnosis by blood test which could at that time take anything from three to nine days.

Robert told us there would be a delay as the stock valuation, which is done on the farm by an independent valuer with vast experience of all categories of farm livestock, was still in progress. We were ushered into the farmhouse kitchen where the farmer's wife was busying herself making cups of tea and coffee for all those assembled, the vet, two vet students, Steve and Adrian from Glasgow University (gaining a once in a lifetime experience), two Army personnel, the valuer, and Sam and myself. She told me it was good to be kept busy as it took her mind off the surreal situation in which she found herself.

Sam and I went outside to look at the lake where coots were charging across the surface of the water defending their territories in a flurry of silver droplets, while a heron was fishing at the far end. A mallard duck with an early brood swam along the margins, trying to keep her ducklings near to protective cover, fearing for their safety. A pair of buzzards wheeled overhead, their wild mewing cries drifting down to us. In the distance a skylark could be heard, sadly a song of the past in my home locality. We stood and took in the morning and reflected that this beautiful and tranquil environment was all too soon to be torn apart by the horror that was to come. A cat carried a mouse around the corner of the barn, crouching low as she saw us, before making off with her prize. The farm dogs came to greet us as we moved towards the cattle sheds. Prior to entering this area we donned our protective clothing. This consisted of waterproof jacket and leggings, all completely covered by a disposable overall. I already knew to my cost, that with physical exertion one could very soon overheat inside this unventilated garb and so I elected to wear only shorts underneath.

There was a yard with a Belgian Blue bull, a lovely chap who came over to talk to us, rolling his eyes as he took in our strange scent. Some 'dry' cows were in with him. These are cows in advanced pregnancy who are no longer lactating, prior to coming into a new lactation when their calves are born. One of these cows actually had calved and had a strong calf at foot. The main milking herd of about 100 Holstein Friesian cows were contained within the pre-milking yard. The buildings and barns around held the followers – young Holstein Friesian heifers which would in due course come into the milking herd. These are usually calves produced from the best lactating cows in the herd, and in the absence of a Holstein bull these cows would have been artificially inseminated. There were also some cross-bred calves which were being reared to produce beef. These calves of both sexes are usually bred from the cows in the herd that are not the best performers, and the Belgian Blue bull would have been kept to father them. There were several sheds and barns containing pens of calves from a few days old to about three or four months old. There was also a bunch of yearling animals still out at grass. All the stock looked very well, and the whole set up was very well managed which made what was to come seem even more of a tragedy.

We assessed as far as we could the best way to do our work, and while we were doing this a man, who we shall call Mike, appeared. Mike worked part-time on this farm as he had done previously on several farms in the vicinity. Foot and mouth had wiped out all these farms, and when this one had gone there would be little work in the area for him. Mike was to be a great help to us and talking to him over the two days we were there proved him to be a fount of farming knowledge.

Robert came out and told us that the paperwork was complete and we could make a start. The vet is the man in charge on the day and he should make all decisions on procedure. Although vastly experienced in abattoir work, Sam and I had killed no cattle in these circumstances up to this point, and were not as familiar as we might have been with the tranquillising of the animals prior to shooting. As cows, as opposed to young cattle, are usually fairly placid creatures, we decided to try and proceed without tranquillisation.

By this time the Belgian Blue bull was lying down chewing his cud on a bed of straw in his pen. I seized the opportunity as he was lying down, took the captive bolt pistol and cautiously approached him, well aware that all bulls, however docile looking, can be unpredictable. He viewed the white-clad figure advancing on him with some suspicion and was clearly undecided whether to rise. As I drew near he decided to show his authority and started to rise. As he did so I stepped smartly forward and shot him. He never heard the shot that killed him. This procedure had gone extremely well which was gratifying as it had been watched by all those on the farm to see if the bull would physically eject me from the pen.

I returned to the body with a pithing cane, which is a solid plastic rod about two and a half feet long, which I inserted into the skull through the hole made by the captive bolt pistol. By pushing with a rodding action the whole length can be inserted into the brain, brain stem and spinal cord. This is done for two reasons: firstly to complete the destruction of the main nervous system of the animal, and secondly to render the forelimbs of the animal less likely to reflex thrashing, thereby reducing the likelihood of damage to the person killing the animal. In my opinion this procedure, which has been part of the slaughtering process since the year dot, is vital to the welfare of both animals and abattoir personnel. It ensures there is no possibility of the animal regaining consciousness prior to having its throat cut, and also vastly reduces the risk of horrendous injury to personnel by reflex kicking, which I have personally witnessed.

Having despatched the bull, we found that the other cattle in the enclosure became skittish to say the least, and so we decided that the rest should be tranquillised. The young vets were enlisted to do this, and they did a marvellous job. The cows were taken into the milking parlour, restrained in batches of ten at a time, injected in the rump with tranquilliser and released into a covered yard to wander about while the drug took effect. This could take anything from five to fifteen minutes depending on the susceptibility of the cow concerned. They eventually became almost comatose, some standing with tongues lolling and drooling saliva. These once beautiful alert creatures were reduced to shambling hulks and tragic though this may seem, at least it made them totally unaware of their impending fate. We found the best procedure was for Sam to shoot them and for me to follow with the pithing cane.

The animals were sorted by age, and those over 30 months old as shown on their passport, went to be rendered or incinerated. Those younger may also have been incinerated or rendered or alternatively may have gone to a licensed land-fill site chosen for its location so as not to cause pollution by seepage into underground water courses. The reason for this separation by age was because bovine animals over thirty months old are considered, by the powers that be, to be at greater risk of harbouring the Bovine Spongiform Encepholopathy (BSE) prion than those under thirty months. It is thought better to incinerate these older animals rather than possibly contaminate even a restricted area such as a licensed land-fill site, with a virtually indestructible prion. The animals were marked with a marker spray and then Mike would drag them with a chain leg shackle. They were collected in a silage clamp according to category. Movements could be seen in the distended bellies of the heavily pregnant cows as the large foetuses kicked out as they slowly suffocated.

So we kept killing and killing and killing and killing. It was the most odd experience – even though I have seen and done so much killing in my life and have become almost immune to it this was a totally different scenario. I suppose the reason must be that hitherto it could be justified because the end result was food for us to eat, but under these circumstances it all seemed so pointless and wasteful of life.

The farmer came over to me and expressed his anguish at seeing his life's work destroyed and the blood lines in the cattle he had nurtured over the years wiped out. He questioned why this irrevocable action was necessary when all cloven-footed livestock for some distance around had already been slaughtered either as foot and mouth suspects or as part of the contiguous cull. He observed that to date he had no sign of disease on the farm and until such sign should present itself he wondered why he could not be just left alone to see if he remained disease-free, particularly as he was no direct risk to any other holding. I had no words of comfort or explanation for him, and could only assure him that we would continue our work as kindly and sympathetically as we possibly could.

The contiguous cull policy of the Ministry whereby all stock is killed on any farm which has land adjoining that of a farm which has disease suspected or confirmed has been the cause of much controversy and inevitably thousands of animals have probably died unnecessarily. Personally I believe the policy to be the correct one, my reasons for this belief will become clear in at least two of my stories, this being one of them. Also in Ireland and France where small outbreaks of the disease were heavily stamped on with contiguous slaughter and the problem was very quickly solved.

The killing went methodically on and, in between batches, I went around the ancillary buildings with a free bullet pistol and shot the calves in their pens. Sometimes one, sometimes two, sometimes four or five a bit older together. This was a very sad thing to have to do – these little animals came over to greet me thinking they were going to be fed or that I might have a bucket of milk with me, and I had to go in and kill them, it was a horrible thing to have to do.

At about this point Robert the vet found an ulcer on one foot of a cow, right up between the digits. He called us over because as meat inspectors we have considerable experience of animal disease. Indeed during this killing I had pointed out various conditions to the vet students as we worked amongst the bodies. (One cow had a quite unpleasant mastitis which is an inflammation of the udder, and another had a condition known as lumpy-jaw, properly called actino-mycosis, which destroys the jawbone and causes the animal to make new bone to compensate for loss of the tensile strength of the jaw). We considered the fairly insignificant lesion on this cow's foot and to facilitate investigation I cut off one of the toes and removed the piece of skin with the lesion in the centre of it. Robert sent this sample and a blood sample from this animal off for analysis. I would say at this point that had it not been for the vigilance of Robert and his two student assistants this lesion could easily have been missed.

By this time it was beginning to get dark and we decided that although there were about 50 cattle still to die, thirty of which were still out in the fields, we would call it a night and return the next day to complete our work.

On our return in the morning we killed the remaining few cattle in the buildings and then went with the farmer and several others to round up a bunch of twenty-eight yearlings, some beef, some dairy, which were out at grass. They were very skittish and we had to do a lot of running and a lot of sweating to eventually drive them into a corralled area made up of galvanised gates. It was decided that as these young animals were so frisky it would be dangerous for Robert and his students to try to tranquillise them. So we now brought our rifles into play, and stood side by side, carefully picking each target. This necessitates waiting until the animal squarely faces you, presenting the perfect head-on target. The first few were very easy as they sought escape from the enclosure, but something seemed to tell them that their heads were vulnerable, and they formed a solid bunch, their heads pointing inwards, presenting their backsides. This meant we had to rotate this formation in order to peel off one at a time to shoot it, which took rather longer than we would have liked.

From a procedure point of view the job had gone very smoothly. By this time the Army personnel had organised the lorries and loading equipment to start to remove the carcasses. This was done very efficiently, with a fore-loading machine sliding under each stiff carcase and hoisting it to then drop it unceremoniously into the bulk container lorry.

The farmer, his arms hanging limply by his sides and a look of devastation on his face, sought me out and thanked me profusely for the job we had done (unbeknown to me he had witnessed some of the slaughter). I said "My friend, we have just wiped out almost everything that you held dear in the world. It takes a man to thank us for doing that". I hugged him and wished him well. He repeated his gratitude to Sam who was coming along behind. We then went through the de-contamination procedure of being steam-cleaned in our waterproofs and having our vehicles disinfected.

Our work completed, we took our leave, mindful of the fact that, when all this frenzied activity had ceased, the farmer would find that in the space of a couple of days his home and business had gone from a noisy vibrant environment to one of silence. I think this must be the worst part of this terrible plague, living with the silence.

Whilst returning home we were asked to carry out a very small but very sensitive task at a nearby smallholding, where a child of the family was extremely ill and needed almost daily hospital visits. The family thought that should they be unlucky enough to go down with foot and mouth they might not be allowed to leave the holding, and this would obviously cause problems with the child's treatment. They had decided that the solution was to have the animals slaughtered even though they were not infected or part of the contiguous cull. Our vet on this occasion was a vet from Langford Veterinary College. Understandably we saw no one from the household and we went about our business as quietly and unobtrusively as we could.

NOTE 1 – It was gratifying (if that is the word to use) to hear later that the lesion found by Robert had indeed been a positive foot and mouth vesicle. I can only hope that this information was passed on to the farmer and it gave him some degree of comfort in the knowledge that the slaughter had not all been in vain.

NOTE 2 – Very sadly I heard much later that this particular farmer had decided not to restock his farm. Possibly this decision was influenced by the "anti-British farmer" attitude which seems to be prevalent in political circles which would appear to favour produce from any country of the world other than Great Britain.

Chapter 6

Easter

Foot and mouth disease was no respecter of Bank holidays, so early morning Easter Sunday saw us heading back up the M5 to North Gloucestershire.

As we travelled it was noticeable that the fields on either side of us were devoid of livestock and as we neared our exit junction we could see dead sheep piled up in gateways awaiting collection. Evidently other slaughter teams had been busy on the previous day.

Arriving early we located our destination but, as there did not appear to be any official presence, we decided to go back to the middle of the pretty little village and await developments. It was a beautiful morning. As it was still early the presence of two strangers was the subject of a certain amount of interest to those inhabitants who were up and about. The peace of the scene was soon shattered by the arrival of three huge bulker lorries travelling in convoy that had come to collect the carcasses we had seen from the motorway.

Shortly afterwards our vet arrived. This turned out to be Robert with whom we had worked in the Forest of Dean. Together we approached the farm down a long lane, rabbits running before us, and met the farmer whose livestock consisted of sheep and poultry. He was a pleasant and very practical man whose only complaint was that although he had fastidiously avoided outside contacts and had taken the required bio-security measures, all this had been to no avail as his flock, which were completely contained within a large lambing shed, were to be part of the contiguous cull regardless. We busied ourselves erecting yet more sheep hurdles and made good use of our knowledge of "spragging". Whilst awaiting the valuer and valuation of the flock, the farmer produced a sickly little lamb which I shot immediately, it being pointless to prolong its suffering. When the valuation was completed it was suggested the farmer should busy himself with his poultry interests and leave us to our work.

We were assisted on this occasion by some very helpful Army personnel and Robert had two very useful veterinary students in tow. The vast majority of ewes with large lambs were running free in the shed whereas the more recently lambed ewes were confined in individual pens around the perimeter of the shed with their one or two lambs. Each pen contained a bucket of water and a separate food container. It was decided that Sam should start work on the large group, whereas I would step from pen to pen despatching the baby lambs and their mothers. It didn't take very long for me to decide to empty the bucket of water as soon as I entered each pen as panic caused either the ewe or the lambs to jump into the bucket, soaking themselves and me.

In this situation I found the best method was to kill the ewe first followed by her youngsters - this saved them from being trampled as a strange white clad figure entered their pen. Completing my unpleasant task I returned to assist Sam with the destruction of the remaining sheep.

The slaughter teams were viewed with disdain in some quarters and dismissed as merely contract killers. Indeed we were contracted to do the governments bidding on behalf of the British people, but while undoubtedly there were some men who carelessly abused their position, in my experience the vast majority were decent people doing a very unpleasant task in the best way possible. I think, unless one possessed a heart of stone, one could not help but be affected by what we were doing. On several occasions, long after the epidemic finished, I spoke to other men who had been killing in other parts of the country. Some of them were not ashamed to say that they had experienced feelings of distaste and the memories of the human and animal trauma would stay with them.

With the job finished and cleansing and disinfecting completed, we said our goodbyes to Robert and his students. We would not work with them again and, should they read this I wish them well wherever they are now. Although we know little about Robert's background (we think he practised in the Cheltenham area) we found his company to be very congenial and he was exceptionally good at what he did.

On most of the jobs we did we found a camaraderie would quickly build between the various groups of official personnel present, but just occasionally, as with the next episode I am about to relate, this was entirely absent, indeed even feelings of distrust and dislike could be engendered.

We were quickly back on the road again and on to the second job of the day. This was down the M5 a bit and off to the right to the village of

Arlingham, which I had seen whilst fire watching from the other side of the river. We were to kill some cull ewes which had been bought for slaughter the previous autumn and had then been over-wintered on some fields which were part of a large dairy farm. The owner of the dairy herd was not the owner of the sheep. The latter lived many miles away and had not been able to visit them since the outbreak of foot and mouth disease and the dairy farmer had, with good reason, become concerned about the wellbeing of these ewes as well as the possible hazard from foot and mouth to his herd. He told me that he had appealed on several occasions to MAFF for the removal of these sheep but, because of the pressure of the current crisis, they had been left to their own devices longer than they should. However their time had now come.

At the site we met an Australian vet who had only recently entered the country and had been asked to help with the crisis. He was accompanied by some agricultural college students. As the dairy farmer had no wish to become involved and the owner of the sheep was long-term absent it fell to the vet, the students and Sam and me to round up the sheep and contain them prior to slaughter. We did not discuss the subject of weaponry before setting out on a quarter of a mile trek along a muddy track with Sam and me carrying all our gear. On arrival at the field the vet announced that only captive bolt pistols and pithing canes should be used. It would have been helpful if he had mentioned this before we set out!

Having constructed a hurdle pen with a division, we turned our attention to the roundup. While the sheep were being gathered from three large fields it became evident they were in extremely poor condition and also infested with sheep scab. This parasitic disease causes severe irritation of the skin and these animals were in such distress that they kept stopping, even while they were being rounded up, to scratch themselves on any available fencepost. Looking around the fields, large amounts of sheep wool could be seen where the poor devils had rubbed themselves nearly naked and subsequently rubbed themselves raw – hence the descriptive name of the disease.

Even in these conditions one of these ewes had managed to produce a lamb. It was dealt with by the vet. For the rest it was a case of methodical slaughter with a captive bolt delivered by Sam while I followed with the pithing cane. This was one the few jobs we were to do where there was no feeling of camaraderie with the vet. Also the agricultural students, who all knew each other, showed little interest in getting to know us.

Returning down the track we met the dairy farmer, who was very relieved at what we had done, and was obviously hoping that the sheep, which were harbouring sheep scab were not also harbouring foot and mouth disease. We wished him good luck and returned to the road where the water bowser and cleansing staff had arrived. Cleansed and disinfected we went on our way.

Chapter 7

Off To Wiltshire

After a lull of ten days, with no reported outbreaks in Gloucestershire, and all the contiguous cull in the area having been completed, we began to think that possibly the disease had been eradicated in this area. Then a call came on Wednesday 25th April telling us that our services were required in a completely new location – this time not very far from the Avebury stones.

It had been late in the afternoon when we got the call and by the time we had collected up our gear and travelled to the site it must have been five o'clock. There were already two Ministry vets at the site of this possible outbreak. One was a Spanish vet I had met before under different circumstances. It was evident that these vets were very keen to get the hundred-odd sheep destroyed as soon as possible. However, their wishes fell on deaf ears as far as the Army personnel were concerned. The Army argued that as they were not yet organised for the disposal of the carcasses the slaughter of the sheep should be postponed.

While the discussion continued the sheep were rounded up twice and twice released by their owner, a contract shepherd who looked after several flocks in the area other than his own.

While we were waiting we chatted with the owner. He told us that if the suspicions were confirmed the implications could be widespread because of the numerous flocks he tended and the wide area over which they were located. We discovered that, on this site, lesions had already been found in the mouths of several of the ewes, between the lower lip and the teeth, and also between the upper lip and the dental pad. Blood tests had also been taken, but the presence of these lesions gave sufficient concern to want the sheep dead prior to the results being known. The site was right on the side of a very busy main road and as we waited I noticed that the presence of so many white clad figures and Army vehicles and personnel was causing many drivers to indulge in the practice of "rubber-necking". A major pileup seemed a strong likelihood. In the end the Army's wishes prevailed and we were asked if we could return early on the morrow to perform our task.

Returning as requested, we found that we were the only people there and we parked in a gateway on the main road to await the others. As we waited, we watched large numbers of rabbits playing and feeding within feet of cars travelling at speed, totally oblivious of the danger. Looking down into the field below us where the sheep were grazing, we saw them start to move towards us. Then some sheepdogs came into view followed eventually by the shepherd's Land Rover. He evidently had another means of access to the ground. With the aid of his dogs, he very soon had the sheep contained, for the third time, in a pen composed of easily handled lightweight aluminium hurdles. The shepherd had obviously equipped himself with the best available equipment. As before, we used the captive bolt method with pithing on the ewes, while the few lambs there were destroyed by barbiturate injection. Sam and I closely examined the ulceration in the mouths, but we were to hear later that the blood tests came back negative.

The bulker lorry arrived and the sheep were duly loaded and sheeted down. The chances of a major road pileup now increased with the spectacle of a large lorry being loaded with dead sheep which made for irresistible viewing. As we were below the level of the road I had visions of cars coming through the hedge on top of us and was glad when we could leave.

It occurred to me then that, should this prove to be a positive outbreak, the transportation of these carcasses through uncontaminated countryside was not a good idea. Indeed it seemed an anomaly, considering the rigorous pressure cleaning and disinfection of both ourselves and our vehicle which we, perfectly correctly, had to undertake after each job.

To my knowledge there were two further killings in this area – one was the famous Bowood estate and the other was another flock belonging to the same shepherd.

Chapter 8

A New Experience

Since the disease was now apparently coming to an end in Gloucestershire and Wiltshire, we offered our services to Taunton and Exeter MAFF offices. Staff at both thanked us for our enquiries, but said they had sufficient staff of their own, at least for the moment. There was still little meat inspection work available so I took a job working for the Meat and Livestock Commission. I was to act as an official presence on the lorries which were collecting stock from all around the country in order to have the livestock killed in accordance with the Government's so-called Welfare Scheme. Initially, I was completely unaware of what the job would involve. It turned out that the hours were often irregular and very long. Sometimes I would leave home at 1am to drive to a given abattoir and would not return until 3am the following morning. However, this was more than compensated for by the pleasure I derived from the company of some really great guys who drove the lorries for the various animal haulage firms involved, some of them employees and some owner-drivers. How they kept going over those frenzied weeks I shall never know.

The restrictions on animal movements, brought in as a consequence of the outbreak of foot and mouth disease, resulted in great difficulties for some farmers. Because stock could not be taken for slaughter in the normal way, winter feed and grazing were at a premium and some farms were very short of food. Also, as no animals were going out, no money was coming in, and cash flow became a problem for many people. In the case of pig fattening

61

units, which are geared to a rotation of young pigs coming in and older pigs going to slaughter, space ran out, necessitating the removal of prime fat pigs at one end and little piglets, sometimes with their mothers, at the other. In an attempt to address these problems the Government introduced the Farm Animal Welfare Scheme .

Under the Scheme, stock was transported under veterinary licence from the farms to abattoirs which for this purpose had to be re-designated as 'killing points'. The licence an abattoir normally holds is to kill animals to produce food for human consumption but under the terms of the Scheme this was no longer the case, carcasses of stock killed under its regulations were destined either for incineration or burial by the thousand in land-fill sites. Stock animals could not be moved to abattoirs as they would cross 'clean' areas and so represented a potential contamination risk.

In my new job I, along with many others, only some of whom were from the meat trade, was to travel on the cattle lorries to the selected farms to match the stock to the movement licence. This was important because the farmers were compensated for the stock they disposed of in this way. However, it was very apparent to me that many of these animals were prime meat animals and should have been slaughtered for food.

Before setting off, the lorry had to be disinfected inside and out. I also had to seal the lorry from the abattoir to the farm, although the purpose of this I found somewhat obscure, bearing in mind that I was seated in the lorry for the whole journey. On arrival I had to unseal the lorry, supervise the loading of the licensed stock and reseal the lorry for the return trip. I also had to disinfect the wheels with a small garden spray as we left the farm.   On arrival at the abattoir the lorry was once again sprayed underneath with disinfectant. It occurred to me that these precautions, however desirable, were somewhat negated by the fact that the animals themselves were potentially contaminated, coming as some of them did from fields adjacent to outbreaks of disease.

Depending on the time of day we arrived at the abattoir the sheep and pigs would either be lairaged for the night or run straight off the lorries to slaughter. This could take place through the abattoir system however, as the site had been designated a killing point, many of the animals were slaughtered outside in specially constructed pens. To make absolutely sure that no animal survived the shooting the plant rule was to also cut all their throats. The carcasses were then shovelled up using the bucket of a large machine and tipped unceremoniously into waiting bulker lorries, destined to be buried in landfill sties. The floor area at the rear of the lorries was liberally coated with sawdust to prevent the seepage of blood onto the road. The large quantity of blood in the bottom of the lorries was due to the incredible weight of bodies tumbled one on top of the other.

The cattle and calves were put through the dressing line. Their skins were removed and sold. Their stomachs and intestines were removed but all other remaining organs were left in the carcase. Depending on size the calves were either left whole or sawn in half like the rest of the cattle. The sides were then further broken down and loaded into lorries to be taken for incineration.

First thing in the morning the jobs were allocated and I would be given the haulage company, the number of the lorry and the driver's name. On my first morning I went to find my lorry, clutching a holdall containing flask, sandwiches, various permutations of clothing, and the necessary paperwork for the trip in one hand, and in the other my garden sprayer for wheel disinfection only to find that I was to ride with two lorries driven by two brothers, both of whom were already known to me. They were amused to see me in a different guise and assured me that, as they were very familiar with the scheme, they would look after me. We were driving the two lorries to Hereford to collect 50 breeding cows.

On arrival at what appeared to be a cattle feed lot, we could see a very modern unit made up of several large asbestos buildings around a central yard. Each unit contained 50 or so beef cattle. The arrival of our large lorries aroused the interest of these cattle and they pushed their heads through the feed bars all the better to see what was going on. One shed contained Belgian Blue heifers, prime beef animals and a picture to see. In the back of the shed I could see a large beef bull. The farmer appeared and I enquired as to the whereabouts of the breeding cows I was to collect. He indicated the Belgian Blue heifers and, noticing the surprised expression on my face, quickly added "Well, there is a bull running with them!" by way of explanation. Apparently, according to Government guidelines this was perfectly acceptable to qualify them for breeding cow status, which meant that they attracted a larger payment than if they had been sold as beef heifers. These particular animals were plenty big and old enough to be mated, but over the ensuing months I saw this charade being played out on many occasions, sometimes with little heifers hardly more than calves themselves. However, who could blame a beleaguered farmer for trying to persuade a vet to licence these young heifers as breeding cows when large amounts of money were at stake?

On many, many more occasions I saw farmers sending cows on the Scheme as cull cows, commanding a fraction of the breeding value, purely because either the licensing vet, or the farmer, or both, were unaware of the criteria of this ill thought out and cobbled together Government scheme. On several of these occasions I encouraged the farmers to re-contact the vet to pregnancy test cows which were evidently pregnant in order for them to claim what was rightfully due to them.

As we were loading the heifers one scrabbled over the feed rail out into the yard, and the farmer, admiring her bid for freedom, told us to go on and leave her behind. Considering the amount of money involved, it was heartening to see his compassionate attitude. However, before we left he took me aside and showed me two very large silage clamps; one completely empty and the other with very little remaining to feed the other shed of cattle. I can only hope that he was able to draw feed from elsewhere.

My second trip highlighted what was soon to become a common problem: how to gain access to some of these isolated farmsteads with the huge cattle lorries necessary to carry large numbers of stock. In some instances it was known in advance that the access was poor and a small lorry was brought along to ferry stock sometimes two or three miles. Alternatively local arrangements to use horsebox and Land Rover were sometimes made. At other times we did not discover the problem until we were on site. The practice of transferring stock from one vehicle to another was later considered a possible hazard. However, bearing in mind that the animals' feet never came in contact with the road when the two vehicles were backed one against the other with one tailboard laid on top of the other to allow the animals to cross over, perhaps those people polishing their trousers in their offices could tell me how else the stock could have been extricated from the premises described without calling in a helicopter.

This particular trip involved the removal of thirty eight cows with their thirty eight suckler calves. Sending the calf with the cow was the third way of claiming breeding cow status, but the farmers were not paid for the calves. The owners of these cows and calves were several brothers who were sick with worry about the position they found themselves in and voiced their pessimism about the future of the small farmer in this country.

Chapter 9

Back to the Killing Fields

As I have already mentioned, Sam and I had offered our services to the Taunton and Exeter MAFF offices sometime previously. Out of the blue one day I received a call from Sam on my mobile phone telling me our presence was requested in Taunton that very afternoon for a meeting and a job as there had been a suspected outbreak in the area. The only problem was that I was on a lorry in the middle of Wales at the time! We decided that the best course of action would be for Sam to drive to Taunton alone that afternoon and I would join him that evening, if possible. As a result I exhorted the lorry driver to put his foot down as I needed to be home as soon as possible.

In the event I did not arrive home until 7pm by which time it was hardly worth setting off for Taunton, so I decided that an early start in the morning would be preferable. I spoke with Sam that evening and learnt that after his meeting with MAFF officials in the afternoon he had been put to work straightaway and had killed about 20 cattle on a farm not far from Taunton. These cattle had been in close proximity to some milking goats, which had already been slaughtered on suspicion of infection. Sam told me that, assisted by three young men, he had confined these young beef cattle in a high sided lane. Apparently the vet in charge did not have any tranquilliser to sedate these cattle and so Sam had to stalk each one with a captive bolt pistol. This can be a difficult and sometimes very dangerous operation, either from the possibility of a charge or from getting trampled or kicked by frightened and milling cattle. We agreed that Sam would find a

B&B for the night and we would meet in the morning to continue the slaughter of more cattle on the same farm.

On my arrival in the vicinity of the farm in the morning I tried to ring Sam for directions but found I had no signal on my mobile phone and had to drive to the top of the nearest hill before I was able to make contact. He told me he had passed the night in a B&B where he felt honoured to be allowed to stay and the owner of which put him in mind of Hyacinth Bucket. He gave me directions to the farm and we were soon talking to the farmer, his son and the auctioneer/valuer. We were to meet the latter on several subsequent occasions. While the valuation was being completed Sam and I assessed the job ahead which consisted of a further 100 cattle on two sites, one close to the farm and one in a covered cattle yard half a mile up a hill track. This was a suckler herd and the site close to the farm held cows with fairly young boss calves while cows with much bigger calves were in the cattle yard.

At the first venue we drove all the cattle into an open plan old fashioned milking shed. We then set up a series of gates so that we could confine six or seven at a time and the vet was able to sedate them. Each batch was released into an open yard in order for the drug to take effect. As each one became oblivious to our presence Sam shot it and I followed with the pithing cane. All went smoothly other than that some of the larger calves did not take kindly to being compressed in this manner and lashed out at the vet with their back hooves, but fortunately he escaped injury. Eventually only one very young calf was left on its own in the pen. For some reason the farmer wanted it to be destroyed with barbiturate.

The farmer's son remained with us throughout on the first killing site but half way through on the second killing site it all became too much for him and he had to leave us. By virtue of what they do for a living farmers can not afford to be sentimental or squeamish. Everything on a farm, other than the cat or the dog, is destined to be slaughtered, at some stage. However, this is normally done at the abattoir out of sight of the farmer concerned. Inevitably he builds up a close relationship with his animals, and for him to see everything on the farm killed at once must be a very traumatic experience.

At the second killing site cattle were again crushed together with gates at one end of the barn to enable the vet to tranquillise them. One large calf decided that injections were not for him and, with a bit of a struggle, managed to squeeze through the feed rail at the front of the shed which gave him free access to a large field. We decided it was better to let him have a run and hope that he would return to his mother, rather than try to chase and catch him. It wasn't long before he came back to peer at us through the feed rail. Sam, anticipating his predictable behaviour, was waiting with his rifle with the fatal shot. On this occasion, as at some other times, it was noticeable that the tranquillisation seemed to have different effects on individual animals. Some became almost comatose very quickly, whereas others appeared to show little effect, and the only difference that I could see was that the animals that showed more signs of stress seemed to resist the action of the drug.

On completion of this job, having cleansed and disinfected, we returned to the Taunton office to be told that we had another job for the afternoon to kill some 500 sheep, part of a larger flock, the remainder of which we would deal with, along with some cattle, the next day. We were accompanied for the afternoon by two young and one older meat inspectors, who had been allocated to assist us. Two came from Kent and one from the Midlands and they all proved to be a great asset to us, helping with the erection of hurdles, the spreading of slaughtered sheep for inspection, and the spraying of carcasses with citric acid, a substance unloved by the foot and mouth virus.

The sheep turned out to be pedigree animals, the majority polled Dorsets and there were some pedigree French 'Inra 401' sheep, which are known for their prolific lambing ability as well as producing large amounts of milk. It was bad enough to kill non pedigree commercial stock, but to kill pure-bred animals of this calibre which had obviously taken many years of selective breeding to produce, seemed particularly devastating. We did however find out later, when talking to the farmer, that he had more of his pure bred sheep elsewhere, which were tended by someone else and were out of range of the contiguous slaughter that we were involved with. One can only hope that there were sufficient numbers left to form the nucleus of a new flock.

The killing took place in a huge barn and by the time we had finished one third of the floor area was covered with corpses, packed together like sardines, stiffening in all sorts of grotesque positions.

By late evening it was time for home. Taunton office had booked us into the Holiday Express, my first experience of a modern form of bed and breakfast, but nevertheless a very convenient base from which we could operate. After a welcome shower and change of clothing we decided to go to a Harvester restaurant on the same site, thus saving us a drive into Taunton. Incongruously there we were served by a Chinese waiter with whom we struck up quite a rapport and who looked out for us on the following evenings. He had a marvellous sense of humour and was able to anticipate our every wish. Returning to the Holiday Express for a nightcap we found that the Army and mostly Navy personnel who were dealing with the logistics of this latest outbreak were also in the same hotel, together with one of the valuers and several externally recruited vets. What started as a nightcap turned into a very pleasurable evening, although we remained mindful that a clear head was imperative for the next day's endeavours.

As I have already mentioned we returned to the same farm to kill the remaining 800 sheep and over 100 cattle. We started with about 100 fat lambs, many of which were fit for market, now alas only to be wasted. The remaining sheep were ewes and lambs, most of which had just or were just on lambing. This is a deliberate strategy on the part of the farmer to make the lambing period as short as possible, so as not to lose too many nights sleep. The vet who was with us on this occasion insisted on killing all the small lambs with barbiturate, including one memorable incident when a ewe was actually producing her lamb at the time of her slaughter and the vet killed the lamb before it could rise and I shot the mother before she could get to her feet. This time we were killing on the floor of a huge silage clamp, which by the time we had finished was packed from end to end with dead bodies.

We then started on the cattle. There were some big beef cattle in one yarded area, some yearlings in a big open fronted barn, and some more big beef cattle running loose in the field below the farmhouse. At the first site there was a cattle crush into which each could be driven to be injected and then released into a large yard to await slaughter. At the second site things were much more difficult: trying to confine flighty young cattle against their wishes. But with the aid of the young Navy boys and the meat inspectors our task was eventually completed. The third site with about thirty biggish cattle only had a high sided lane in which we could confine them both for tranquillising and slaughter. Two of the cattle decided they did not wish to stay there anymore and, after climbing the side of the lane, they took off across the nearest field. Unlike young dependent calves with their mother, these cattle had no reason to return and, having been thoroughly spooked by the presence of so many white clad figures, had no intention of doing so. The remaining cattle in the lane had by now started to collapse and it was decided to slaughter these and give the escapees time to settle down. We then managed to drive one back to the lane where it was promptly shot but the other would only come as far as the top of the bank and refused to descend into the lane. After several unsuccessful tries the vet eventually managed to get a needle into it, and although it was not completely comatose Sam stalked it with the captive bolt and shot it whereupon, with concerted effort, we rolled it the edge of the bank and tumbled it down to join its fallen comrades.

Returning to the farm we chatted to the farmer and his wife who had maintained complete composure throughout. We had not until now had the opportunity to talk to the farmer. He had busied himself throughout the day with his dog and his quad bike, supplying us continuously with batches

72

of sheep exactly when we wanted them. He did a marvellous job. Whilst chatting over a final cup of tea I discovered that he knew several of my shooting friends in the area and it was rather surprising that I had not met him before. His wife hugged each of us and thanked us for our efforts. She said they had not known at the outset what to expect, but our professional and sympathetic approach had made the slaughter not as bad as she had anticipated.

I thought as we left that the farmer and his wife, with the part time assistance of their daughter, ran an enterprise of some 1300 sheep and well over 100 cattle on their own, which goes to show how hard smaller farmers have to work in order to make a living.

Returning to our hotel we followed our routine of hot showers and change of clothing. Once again we adjourned to the Harvester and were welcomed by our Chinese waiter friend, who I think had kept a table ready for us. The establishment was somewhat busier than before, this being a Bank Holiday weekend. After eating we spent another pleasant evening in the bar of the hotel, swapping stories with the Army and Navy personnel about our normal daily occupations.

Chapter 10

No Reprieve For Our Lambs

The next morning we went into the office to see what the day might bring for us. We heard that there was a flock of some three hundred sheep that may or may not have to be killed as a contiguous slaughter, but all we could do was wait until decisions were made.

Eventually the word came to go ahead.

Our destination, not far from Taunton, was easy to find as it was very close to a shoot that I sometimes go to in the winter. A friend of mine, who owns the farm where the shoot takes place, breeds pedigree Suffolk sheep and I thought it might be a good idea to ring him and warn him how close the potential infection had spread to his property. He would obviously already be taking great care of his stock, but my advice would be to allow nobody entry to his premises.

The three hundred sheep concerned had been grazing a large open parkland and on our arrival we could see that preparations were well under way with the usual hurdle constructed pens. The owners, a father and son, thoughtfully asked us if the layout was to our satisfaction. It was pleasant to see that even under stressful conditions they were mindful of our needs. The son, a lad of about 20, was incredibly strong and had developed a technique for carrying three hurdles at once, formed in a triangle around him, and then proceeding to step over hurdles already erected to arrive at his destination. Most average men would be happy to carry one hurdle over flat ground. The sheep were now gathered with the aid of two collie dogs from a very wide area of parkland interspersed with trees and little coppices. This seemed to go well and all we had to do was watch.

Our vet for the day was a young South African who had been en route from South Africa to Saudi Arabia. He had been due to take up a veterinary post there on a huge dairy complex situated in the desert where all feed had to be brought to the cattle. As he was passing through this country he volunteered his services in response to the emergency situation. He was a very practical and efficient young man and, having asked us to demonstrate our technique with the ewes and lambs, he indicated he was more than happy for us to proceed, with no mention of injecting the small lambs. Prior to commencing, I asked the farmer if he wished to witness the slaughter. He said that he would stay, but at a distance. However, his son, who was so physically strong, said it was rather more than he wanted to see and took his leave. The farmer's collie dog remained on the periphery of the pens throughout the slaughter ensuring that nothing escaped either through, or over, the hurdles.

Parting off thirty or so at a time, we started in the usual manner ejecting the dead lambs first over the sides of the pen and then, on completion of each batch, collapsing the pen and spreading the ewes to facilitate veterinary examination. We found one lamb with acute ulceration between its digits on one foot and around the coronary band but, as it was very swollen, the considered opinion was that it was probably 'orf'. The job proceeded smoothly enough and on completion we removed the hurdles. After spraying the carcasses they were covered with plastic sheeting. This was the only time I saw this done. Whether it was to protect the carcasses from scavengers, or to hide the carnage from public gaze as we were close to a housing development, I do not know.

We thought the job was completed and well managed only to find how wrong this turned out to be. Later that evening ,while relaxing in the hotel, the vet received a telephone call to say that two tiny lambs had appeared at the slaughter site, where the carcasses remained for collection the next day, and were bleating for their mother. The phone call had come from two Navy guys who were at the site. They had managed to contain these lambs and were awaiting instructions. I elected to go with the vet in my vehicle to investigate the situation.

It would appear that these lambs, which had just been born, must have hidden themselves, as young animals do, in one of the many small coppices. They then waited until all was quiet and they were hungry and emerged from their hiding place to try to find their mother who must have been slaughtered earlier in the day. Tragic as this event may appear, it was in fact nobody's fault, bearing in mind this flock of sheep had been lambing recently prior to the slaughter, whilst others had not yet lambed. This meant nobody knew exactly how many lambs there should have been. It was fortunate that this site was being all-night guarded, which did not happen very often, otherwise these orphans would not have been noticed until the next day. As it was I quickly despatched the twins. For them there was to be

77

no last minute reprieve, as in the case of Phoenix, the white calf rescued by Mr Blair for political expediency with the General Election looming. Despite the fact that thousands of other calves and multitudes of other animals had already died, many probably unnecessarily, an exception was made for Phoenix!

Chapter 11

Non-events

The next day we were called into the office in Taunton once again and were told that there was a job which was very politically sensitive. This job involved 900-plus cattle which were to be part of the contiguous cull as the premises, it was alleged, had been visited by a man whose business it was, along with various other farming functions, to disbud the horns of young calves. This occupation necessarily involved him travelling from farm to farm. He had had some connection with the herd of milking goats I mentioned in chapter nine. Unfortunately, the stock on all the farms he had subsequently visited was due for slaughter. This must have placed this individual in an invidious position through no fault of his own. The owner of the 900 cattle had decided to fight the diktat of the Ministry and had parked all his farm vehicles across the driveway to his premises.

We were told in the office that all sorts of legal appeals were taking place, but that when a positive conclusion was reached the slaughter should be carried out with all speed. To this end it had been decided that Sam and I should be assisted by a slaughter team of four people comprising a vet, a Ministry Field Officer, a farmer who had already lost his stock who acted as a drover, all from Devon and a slaughterman from Cornwall. This team was very experienced, having already been working for some weeks around the Devon area where the disease had been much worse than in Somerset. We were introduced to them in the canteen. Inevitably there was an atmosphere of mutual suspicion as we withdrew to separate tables, but gradually a thaw

79

took place as we drank our coffee and we began to swap stories and experiences and find out a little more about each other.

Our instruction was to proceed to the village of Dulverton, trying to keep as low a profile as we could, to await developments. The farm concerned was apparently only a very few miles away. It was a beautiful spring day and those of you who have visited this picturesque village will know exactly how delightful our surroundings were.

Although early in the season there would normally by now have been a sprinkling of tourists but because of foot and mouth restrictions there were no strangers, apart from ourselves, in the village. Our presence inevitably aroused interest and, as we toured the shops in the village and enjoyed a coffee in the local hostelry, we were questioned on several occasions as to the reason for our visit. We thought this must have been obvious, given the media interest in the case, but we stuck to the terms of our brief and did not comment. We found out later that, had the legal appeals failed, many of the villagers were prepared, on a given signal, to rush to the farm concerned to prevent anyone from carrying out the contiguous cull.

Sam and I adjourned to the riverbank to watch the trout rising to early flies. We waited and waited and waited. Several times we made contact with the office and were assured that it was all about to happen. At 6pm we were told to stand down, but to remain in a state of readiness for the next day.

After a short wait the next morning, we were told that there had been a legal stay of execution and we could stand down. I returned to my temporary lodgings in Clevedon and after a few days break in order to become "clean" I returned to work on the Welfare Scheme.

Foot and mouth was still raging in Devon and in other parts of the country. I felt it only fair to inform the people running the Scheme that, should there be any further outbreaks in the Gloucestershire or Somerset areas, I might be called back again at a moment's notice.

It was not long before Sam and I were told to standby for a possible outbreak in Somerset near Bridgwater, although we had to wait for confirmation. The isolated outbreak was confirmed, but we were told that our services would not be needed, as the infected farm was to be dealt with by yet another vet I knew. The four adjoining farms then became the subject of a contiguous cull. Two of these farms were farmed by two brothers one of whom was a qualified slaughterman, and it was agreed by Taunton office that he would slaughter the stock on all four farms. This of course led to the situation where this man not only killed his brother's cattle but also had the unpleasant task of killing his own suckler cows and calves, some forty in number.

Much later, when back at my regular work, I met Clarence, the slaughter man concerned. He is a character well known in the local area for his alternative lifestyle and tremendous sense of humour. He told me that among the animals he had undertaken to slaughter was a fourteen year old

Aberdeen Angus cow which had been with him all her life and had become a great pet. Although she was not of a sunny disposition and, several times during her life when freshly calved had tried to kill him, he thought the world of her and it had upset him greatly to have to kill her.

However, this was an occasion when the policy of slaughtering adjoining farms to an outbreak stopped the disease in its tracks as there were no further outbreaks in this area.

Ulceration on cows tongue—a symptom of Foot and Mouth

Ulceration on sheep's tongue

Pedigree Suffolk ewes unlucky enough to live in the next field to an outbreak

Sometimes it was difficult to reach the farms to collect the stock

Even uninfected pedigree Aberdeen Angus bulls were slaughtered

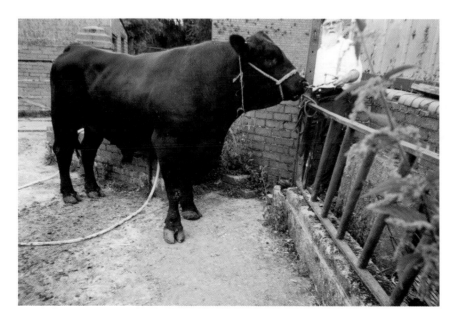

Many generations of these animals had been bred by this farmer

Sheep were left in all sorts of locations for collection—so much for bio security

The vet had been in before us, killing and bagging the animals with symptoms

Maggots of the green bottle fly have attacked this sheep.

Because shearers could not get to the animals to remove the fleeces, animals ended up being eaten alive —see chapter 23

This poor animal could not stand up but like so many others had been deemed fit to travel by the licensing inspecting vet

These pigs had been badly managed by their owner and were starving—see chapter 25.

Conditions for working could be very difficult

Four wheel drive transport was required to access many of the
areas where we had to work.

The farm falls silent

Leaving a large amount of dead weight to be transported away.

Chapter 12

Out and About

We were heading for Hereford again with two small lorries when we heard that there might be some difficulty with access. As we neared the site we could see several fields adjoining the farm completely churned to mud: ewes and lambs had eaten every last blade of grass and must have been relying entirely on hay and concentrates.

The owners turned out to be a husband and wife team. The licence was for 200 cull ewes and I enquired where they were to be found. The farmer indicated the mothers of the lambs, whose ages ranged from a few weeks to half grown. It was very unusual for the farmer to keep lambs of this age for two reasons. Firstly, because they were hardly old enough to be weaned and would probably go back as a result and secondly, because the price of a cull ewe was a fraction of that of a breeding ewe. The ewes concerned were top of the range large Suffolk cross sheep and appeared to be maybe only in their second lambing season. The farmer told me that on another site he had a similar number of much older ewes but, for all sorts of intricate reasons, he had no choice but to dispose of the younger sheep. However, he was desperate to try to salvage something from the disaster, so he had opted to retain the lambs and try to wean them early. This was the one and only time amongst many visits that I encountered such a strange decision and I am sure he would have been better off counting out 200 of the smallest lambs to send with the 200 ewes. This would have given him more money as breeding ewes commanded higher compensation. He would then have retained the oldest of the lambs, bearing in mind many of the ewes would have had twins, and these older lambs would have stood a much better chance of thriving. He also would have had more money to buy feed or restock.

Having loaded the sheep, which because of their large size took up most of the floor space, we set off, leaving the farmer and his wife sitting on their quad bike looking very dejected. Because we had separated the lambs from their mothers, there was a cacophony of plaintive bleating from the lambs in response to the deeper calls from the ewes in the lorry. The little lambs raced along the road hedge trying to keep up with the lorries until they came to the end of the field and could go no further, but we could hear their cries for some considerable distance.

As a result of the movement restrictions on animals at this time it was not possible to go from farm to farm collecting stock, even if they were in close proximity. This sometimes meant visiting the same area twice in one day. Inevitably also, this sometimes meant travelling long distances to pick up relatively few animals. Wherever possible, small lorries were used for these jobs, but sometimes we had to take huge animal transporters which were then returning virtually empty.

On one such occasion we had to collect five breeding cows. On arrival we encountered five seven or eight month old heifers, licensed as breeding cows because they had been seen to be running with the bull. Unless the bull was of diminutive proportions the heifers were so small that they would have been hard put to support its weight, never mind become mothers! They should never have been licensed as breeding cows and it might have been thought that the farmer had duped the vet into licensing the animals in order to gain the additional monies. It has to be said that this was one of the very few occasions where I witnessed blatant abuse of the Scheme. I believe that local vets were under such pressure at this time that some licences were issued without the animals being seen, which resulted in these anomalies. In other cases we were loading animals that could not even stand up, but they had been pronounced fit to travel. The good and conscientious vets would assess the animals to be transported and if necessary would put down those deemed unfit to withstand the journey using barbiturate or possibly a twelve bore shot gun. These carcasses would be collected under a parallel Scheme and the farmer would be paid in any case.

On the next day, near Talgarth, we collected six cows and four calves; four cows with their calves were paid for as breeding cows and the remaining two had had their calves weaned away from them that very morning. In happier times as young cows they would have returned to the bull for their next pregnancy and it was obvious that they were potential breeding cows, but because they had no calf at foot or had not been seen by the vet running with a bull they were deemed only to be cull cows and as such could command only about a quarter of what their companions would fetch.

A few days later we were heading for a hill farm right on top of the world near Rhayader. There were fantastic views in all directions. The fields around the farmstead had been grazed down to the earth and, because of the restrictions, the ewes and lambs could not be returned to the hill grazing beyond. As a result they were rapidly running out of food. Little hay can be made on these high farms and so a lot of the winter feed has to be bought in from lower and lusher holdings, which works only if you have money to pay for it. Therefore, with no money coming in and probably no money in reserve, many farmers were at their wits end. This particular farm was run by a farmer, his wife and two sons, one of whom was still at school.

We had come to remove some 170 ewes with their lambs and just four suckler cows with their calves. The farmer observed to me that, in spite of all his endeavours and with the assistance of his family, over the previous year the farm's profit would amount to no more than enough to pay for a good evening out for him and his family. This was, of course, before the outbreak of foot and mouth, so one could only surmise what his position would be in the wake of this epidemic. It also made one wonder, and I discussed this with Andy the driver on the way home, what makes men struggle so hard against the odds for so little reward. The answer can only be that these rugged hill men love the space and solitude of their environment and probably coming from generations of similar men would find it very difficult, both practically and emotionally, to change occupation.

Chapter 13

Out and About Again

Our next destination was Builth Wells, the home of the Royal Welsh Agricultural Show, which was heading for its centenary in 2004.

We left Bristol at 4.30am with two lorries and by the time we arrived in the Brecon Beacons the early morning sun was beginning to clear the river mist, showing the Beacons in their full glory and promising a beautiful hot May day. After crossing a picturesque river bridge over the Usk, we came to a railway bridge over the road, which announced a height restriction of fifteen feet. Both lorries were known to be fifteen feet three inches high. It was decided that, in order to avoid a long detour, a very tentative passage in the centre of the bridge should be attempted. Sadly, the road rose as it passed under the bridge and as I stood in the centre of the road up ahead to direct operations I could see the gap of daylight narrowing from about six inches to a coat of paint. Fortunately, the move was successfully completed with no damage. I never cease to marvel at the skill of these drivers maneuvering their huge vehicles in incredibly tight situations.

We still had approximately five miles to go to the farm down a road, like so many others, where the lorry filled it from bank to bank. We always had to hope that there would be sufficient room at the end for the lorries to turn around. The alternative would have been reversing, sometimes for as much as ten miles, to escape. This situation fortunately never occurred. After travelling about three of the five miles we encountered a big tree limb growing across the road, precluding further progress. Finding ourselves in something of a valley there was no signal on my mobile phone. I elected to run to the nearest house up a hill, frightening the good lady occupant to death with my sudden appearance at her back door at seven o'clock in the morning. This in a locality where strangers must be few and far between. From there I was able to ring the farmer who came to meet us with his tractor and fore-loader, and a very blunt chainsaw with a loose chain. He removed the offending limb allowing passage with care. Further on we had to pass under some very low telephone wires, which I climbed up and lifted over the roof of the lorries.

After a succession of low branch removal on some silver birch trees, we finally arrived at the farm. Six hundred very hungry ewes with their lambs were to be taken. We had loaded about half of these on one lorry when the farmer's wife, who had heard from outside sources that there might be doubt about payment, asked me if I could guarantee their money. Not being in a position so to do, I rang the Scheme co-ordinator in Bristol who was also not able to give this assurance and the suggestion was that she should ring the helpline of the Scheme to advise her. All this was taking time. These sheep were destined to die that day and the abattoir would be waiting for them. The drivers were beginning to look at their watches. A 99% assurance of payment was given by the helpline and we proceeded to load the remaining sheep keeping, as far as we could, the ewes and lambs separate. There appeared to be a slight deficit in the number of lambs in relation to the number of ewes, bearing in mind how difficult it was to count them as they ran up the tailboard of the lorry. As a precaution against payment being docked, two tiny little pet lambs, which were being bottle reared, were commandeered to make up the numbers.

After a cup of tea we commenced the return journey. All was well until we arrived at the telephone wires. Now beginning to push against the clock we completely forgot our incoming manoeuvre with the result that the farm, and maybe others, lost their telephone lines. We could not turn around and obviously we could not ring to tell them what had happened so we continued on our way. We then arrived at the first tree from which the limb had been removed that morning. Due to the difference in the camber of the lane, and exacerbated by the weight of sheep on board, the first lorry became firmly wedged against the flat cut edge of the limb. Two courses of action were open to us. We could rip off part of the top deck of the lorry or one of us would have to return on foot to the farm for help. As I was the oldest by far, I was the one elected to run the two miles up and down hills in the hot May sunshine wearing a pair of Wellington boots to get assistance. Having been quite good at long distance running in my youth, and forgetting the unsuitable footwear and the intervening passage of time, I thought my ability to cover this distance quite quickly would not be a problem. However, in the event, I arrived in a dishevelled and extremely overheated state, unable to talk coherently with my feet feeling as though they were on fire, so much so that I had to retire to a little stream running behind the farmhouse to cool down and recover my powers of speech. While in the recovery position I was regarded with some curiosity by the farmer's wife as to the reason for my return. I was able eventually to explain our predicament and the reason why we could not phone back to the farm. She said that her husband had left the yard but that she might be able to contact him. This she managed to do and after a short while the farmer reappeared. I gave him a quick résumé of what had happened and, having considered the problem, he decided that he would have to ring his neighbouring farmers (using his mobile) for permission to cross their land because foot and mouth was raging as close as over the next hill and everyone was very twitchy about cross contamination. Having obtained permission he was then able to bypass the lorries which were obstructing the lane and come at the offending tree from the side. Rearming himself with tractor, chainsaw, ropes and chains, he set off across the fields and I returned on foot along the lane.

The stump of the severed limb was so wedged against the side of the lorry that it was impossible to insert the chainsaw to remove any more, so the decision was taken to fell the whole tree. I volunteered to climb up on the roof of the lorry with the chainsaw to sever as many overhanging limbs of this tree as I could reach. I was now working some twenty feet above the ground and dragged the cut branches across the top of the lorry to deposit them over the hedge and into the field on the other side of the lane. During this process some of the leafy boughs protruded through the ventilation slots on the sides of the lorry and were eagerly consumed by the hungry sheep inside. Having removed as much weight as we could from the top of the tree we then attached chains from the top of the trunk to the back of the tractor and then started to cut the trunk at the base, pulling at the same time with the tractor to drag it away from the lorry. Saying goodbye yet again we moved off with only one final obstacle ahead – the railway bridge. This was negotiated extremely carefully, but in the event the weight of sheep had taken the lorry down on its springs and this gave us more room for manoeuvre.

We had not driven very far before we received a call from the owner of the abattoir asking for an estimated time of arrival as the place was at a standstill awaiting our cargo. He must have also contacted the owner of the lorry who then came on the line enquiring as to the extent of the damage done by the tree to his vehicle. Luckily, we were able to reassure him that the damage was minimal under the circumstances.

Postscript

On all these trips I carried a disposable camera and took many photographs. About a week after the last story, when the developed pictures arrived, my wife looked at them first. She found a photo of one of the drivers in the middle of a lane with his backside in the air and his trousers around his ankles. She enquired as to whether I had taken this photograph and I said that I must have done. On reflection however I realised I had no recollection of doing so, and eventually it dawned on me that whilst I was exerting myself running in the hot sunshine the two drivers had become bored with the wait and had amused themselves by borrowing my camera from my bag, taking the photograph and returning the camera, all without my knowledge.

Chapter 14

Back to Somerset

Mid-June and there had been a further outbreak near the village of Stawley in Somerset, very close to the county border with Devon. As there had been several outbreaks on the Devon side of the border, it had been decided that the same slaughter team that had dealt with those should cross the border and continue on one or two farms in Somerset. After days of anticipation we were called to Taunton to deal with, initially, 28 cattle with the possibility of 11 more on another farm.

Although we did not arrive until 4pm we had a further wait for the vet to arrive. During this time we chatted to the farmer and his son who were bitterly complaining about the attitude of the Australian vet whom they had already met. We asked where he was and were told that he was on an adjacent farm which had been cleared out the day before because of an outbreak and where the eleven cattle already mentioned had escaped slaughter and were being allowed to settle again, maybe for us to kill the next day.

The vet eventually appeared at about six o'clock walking across the fields. Arriving at his car, which he had left outside the farm, he gathered up his bits and pieces and appeared ready to make a start. Sam and I, with the farmer and his son, rounded up some of the 28 beef cattle, confining them in a small yard with a cattle crush in it. These animals were fairly wild and were obviously not fond of strangers clad in white in their midst. We introduced the first one into the crush and the vet duly injected it with tranquilliser. We released this animal into a large open yard to wait for the drug to take effect. The vet then proceeded to stand right in front of the cattle as we tried to get another one into the crush, spooking the whole bunch. He then seemed to become absorbed in the bottle of sedation, peering at it for some time and eventually, without a word of explanation, walked out of the yard and away leaving Sam and I and the farmer and his son looking at each other wondering what was going on.

We waited for nearly an hour for him to reappear, during which time I shot and pithed the first animal. We noticed that the bottle of sedation was broken and wondered if he had also accidentally injected himself. Eventually Sam and I went looking for him, having disinfected ourselves to go back out to the road. We found him chatting to some other people out on the road about another job, seemingly oblivious to the fact that he had left us waiting in limbo for all that time. Suddenly he announced that he had only one more bottle of sedation left, saying he would have to reduce the dose to make it last. Returning to the yard, he very slowly and methodically injected about 15 more cattle. Following this he announced that he now only had some small animal sedative left which might do about two more cattle. Predictably the supply then ran out and the last beast to be sedated was so stressed it leapt from the crush, rushed down the yard and crashed into the gate at the other end, knocking off one of its horns in the process. By this time, Sam and I thought that we must take charge, or we would be there all night. The farmer was getting very restless and something had to be done. The remaining beef cattle and one cow and calf could not be sedated and they were very wild, particularly the mother of the calf, so, in order to save life and limb on our part, we suggested that Sam should shoot them in the barn with his rifle. Whilst Sam did this I started on the sedated cattle, only about half of which were dopey. The rest had to be stalked and shot. This I accomplished with the exception of one black Aberdeen Angus heifer which, with one eye closed but seemingly still very aware of her surroundings, would charge every time I approached her. Having finished in the barn, Sam came and shot her with the rifle to save us from any injury. This just left only the cow with her young calf alive. She was so aggressive that when we tried to open the door of the shed she would charge the door on the inside. As we could not shoot her in the shed, because there were no windows or apertures through which to put the rifle, and there was no way you would want to stand in the open doorway, we decided to release her into the yard. This was easier said than done. The first thing to do was to ask the vet to stand outside the yard. Sam also stood outside the yard with the rifle at the ready. I elected to push open the door and then flatten myself on the wall outside out of her sight. She came out of that shed like a Spanish bull being released into the ring, followed closely by her calf. She went so far down the yard that, by the time she saw me and started to charge, she had given me the necessary time to make my escape. While in mid charge Sam shot her, needing then only a couple of seconds to drop the calf behind her. The vet went out to cleanse himself by his car and the farmer and his son came out again to thank us and shake our hands, assuring us there was no ill will in our direction.

The next day in the office we were tentatively asked how we had got on with the Australian vet. We did not say very much, but I think our faces spoke volumes. It appeared that he had moved up from Devon where he had been working on foot and mouth. If our experience was anything to go by I expect they were only too glad to see the back of him and they must have warned the Taunton office of his inefficiency.

Chapter 15

To Kill, Kill and Kill Again

Our next assignment was to kill nearly 400 sheep, mostly ewes and lambs with a few of last year's lambs, on a farm at Ashbrittle. These were confined in a large barn and we had to erect some small pens in order to divide them up into smaller batches. Before we could start, MAFF personnel had to take some blood samples. The owner of the sheep was a young man who rented the farm but lived elsewhere. He had a further flock of sheep some distance away which we would kill some days later. Over and above his sheep enterprises he also fed and looked after a large pig unit for somebody else. He was very down in the mouth about it all and was concerned that all the pigs would have to be killed as well, because of his connection with them, but in the end this turned out not to be the case.

Having completed the job I looked back at the barn in which we had been working. The whole of one side of it was covered with the largest white wisteria I have ever seen. This was in full bloom and making a magnificent sight. We cleansed ourselves thoroughly and then departed.

Not very far away our second job for the day was around 1400 sheep on a farm which had just achieved its organic status. The sheep were on three different sites, two batches comprising ewes and lambs and the third just ewes. We decided to make a start on the latter. They were penned against a gateway in the corner of the field, apparently secure. Although the gap under the centre of the gate was quite large it seemed unlikely that these large ewes would crawl under it. In the event however, while we were preoccupied slaughtering their fellows, three of them managed to squeeze under the gate and set off up the road. It would have been pointless to chase them, but we had to do something. So, very slowly and carefully, I edged them towards a small, conveniently situated, grassy lane and fortunately they seemed happy to graze the grass on the sides of it. This lane appeared to turn and run parallel to the road but I had no way of knowing how long it was or whether there were any gates or barriers to stop their progress. As luck would have it, as I moved forward I could see a gate up ahead across the lane. As the sheep reached the gate and I drew closer to them, they considered rushing back pass me. I shouted to Sam to proceed along the road, hoping he would be able to lean over the hedge and shoot them. This he managed to do and very quickly the three sheep were dead. It was decided that we should leave them where they lay, rather than return them to the field, because the gate concerned was in fact the entrance to the field where on the next day we were due to kill 1000 sheep. Returning, we finished the first batch of sheep and moving on to the second site we killed a number of ewes and lambs. Our vet for the day took great interest in my .22 pistol and commented on the efficiency and ease of kill with the short .22 bullets.

As there were just over a 1000 sheep on this farm still to be killed and they had yet to be gathered and hurdles erected for their confinement, it was decided to call it a day and return in the morning. After the usual cleansing and sterilising everyone went their separate ways leaving Sam and I sitting in our vehicle on the road chatting and considering the day's events. Everything was now quiet around us and we saw a pair of carrion crows land in the field by the dead sheep. After a good look round to assess that all was safe, they came and landed on the carcasses by the gate and started to feed on the bits of clotted blood adhering to the bodies. We drove them off but knew it would not be long before they returned to feast on this bonanza. This was only a contiguous slaughter, but it makes you wonder how many similar piles of bodies, sometimes left for many days before collection, were preyed upon by various scavengers with the very real risk of the further spread of infection.

On arrival the next day we busied ourselves helping with the erection of hurdles. When all was ready the farmer began to gather the sheep. The MAFF staff were busy taking samples. When this was completed we began our work using our well rehearsed technique of catching all the lambs, shooting them as previously described, and dropping them outside the pen for the vet to examine their mouths and feet for possible lesions. Starting then on the mothers, we shot them in such a way that they lay only one deep on the ground. This was to prevent them climbing one over the other and possibly suffocating those underneath. We would then collapse the pen to facilitate the veterinary examination of the mothers. Sadly, we heard that elsewhere sheep were being shot four or five deep. In these circumstances it would be very difficult to be sure that all of them had been shot, leading to animals being suffocated by overlying bodies in some cases and in others to animals getting up and running away after the slaughter.

We continued until mid afternoon when a call came from the Taunton office asking if we were in a position to kill some cows on another farm, a few miles away, where there had been a confirmed outbreak. As we had almost finished we said that we would get there as soon as possible. While we were collecting up our gear the farmer went with his tractor box to collect the three bodies lying by the far gate of the field from the night before. We were not surprised to see that all the skin and flesh from the heads of two of the ewes had been eaten overnight by a fox, a badger or possibly a dog. Disinfection over, we drove on to the next assignment.

This turned out to be 70 odd cattle, which comprised mostly milking cows with a few followers. Valuation was still going on when we arrived and so we had time to walk around and take stock. There was a lovely old stone built farmhouse with a large range of outbuildings all sadly neglected and run down. It was evident that the front door had not been used for some time as a bramble bush grew right across it. The plan, it seemed, was that the cows would be driven a few at a time into the milking area. They would then be tranquillised by the vet and released into a holding yard for the drug to take effect. On one side of this yard was a pool of liquid bovine excrement about 20 feet long by 10 feet wide. As the cows stumbled about in a dazed condition they seemed drawn to this pond like a magnet. I knew that if they collapsed into the pond when shot their thrashing legs would cover all about with liquid manure. In an attempt to prevent this from happening I tried, without much success, to keep them moving to a drier area.

With Sam shooting, and me pithing, we clambered over the melee of dead and tranquillised bodies. All of a sudden, and probably because by this time we were very tired from our day's work, my legs were kicked clean from under me and I went down into a forest of thrashing legs, any one of which could have killed me. Had it not been for Sam's quick reaction I could have been a dead body amongst many others. Grabbing a handful of my overalls he yanked me to my feet, muttering something about silly old buggers, but he probably saved my life. Never before, or since, have I been so covered in bovine faeces as I was on that farm and never before have I so looked forward to a hot shower. When collecting my room key I noticed the girl on the reception desk giving me an odd look. It wasn't until I looked in the mirror in my room that I realised that she had probably noticed a large lump of cow manure at the base of my neck that had evidently been overlooked when cleansing in the field.

Only one of the cows was showing lesions on tongue and feet. Later discussions with veterinary friends revealed that it is by no means unusual that one animal can become heavily infected although it may not be until some hours later that others start to show symptoms.

Chapter 16

Plenty Left to Kill

The next morning saw us returning to a further farm to kill some sheep which were in a field adjoining the one where we had killed the cattle the previous day. They turned out to be some beautiful pure bred Suffolk ewes and two Suffolk rams which were running with them. When I asked the farmer where he had obtained the rams he told me the name of a friend of mine who produces pedigree Suffolk rams. It is bad enough killing the commercial non pedigree stock, but it is much worse destroying animals which have been carefully bred over many generations aiming for perfection in breed characteristics. The morning was one of the hottest June days of the year and, dressed as we were, I for one overheated to a point where I was feeling sick and almost passed out, but fortunately I was just about able to complete the job.

The afternoon took us not very far away to a hundred odd sheep and thirty or so young beef cattle. The sheep, which were already penned, were soon accounted for. We then moved down to some farm buildings where the cattle were in a large covered yard. They were very wild and there was some difficulty in containing them in order for the Ministry vet to tranquillise them. While we waited for the drug to take effect the lady farmer gave us tea and biscuits. We chatted and it emerged that she was the owner of the 11 escaped cattle mentioned in a previous chapter, which were originally part of a bunch of 15 very wild young cattle. Four of these had been killed but 11 made a run for it. The Ministry had then apparently caught up with seven more, leaving four at large as we spoke. We offered to shoot them with a deer rifle but it was decided to allow them to settle again. I understand they were finally killed in the normal way.

She also told us that she had noticed that reports on the foot and mouth epidemic were disappearing from the newspapers and that when she rang several of them to say the disease was still rampant in this area they could not have been less interested. Evidently the decimation of our rural way of life does not sell papers and is of little interest to a large proportion of the urban population of this country. Perhaps they should be reminded that the farming communities largely kept us fed through two world wars. Unfortunately current Government policy actively encourages farmers to leave the industry, or pays them to do nothing at all. This means that when a catastrophe strikes, and strike it will, we will be unable to feed ourselves, a situation which would take many months in the case of growing crops, or years in the case of livestock farmers, to remedy.

Returning to the matter in hand, the cattle were by now heavily sedated with the exception of one which was rampaging around the barn while we shot its fellows. Why this animal had not succumbed to the drug I do not know. As it was not safe to use the rifle in this circumstance, and there was no way that this animal was going to allow itself to be confined again, Sam and I and the bullock ended up in a rather undignified scrum in order to restrain it long enough for Sam to shoot it.

The next day we returned to the office in Taunton to replenish our supplies and were asked to kill two flocks of sheep, both belonging to the same owner, a total number of about 270. The first flock was corralled in a gateway adjoining a lane and blood testing was already underway when we arrived. After a wait of about an hour we killed about 100 ewes and lambs. Whilst doing so we were regarded with some suspicion, but no particular concern, by three horses, which were grazing in the same field. It seems odd with all this death that they should remain alive, but it is of course only cloven footed animals that are susceptible to the disease. When we had finished we had to wait for the pressure cleaner and water bowser to arrive. There had evidently been a minor accident involving the trailer with the water bowser on it. This was driven by two entrepreneurial young men who, seeing an opportunity to make some money, had obtained this cleansing equipment and had followed us from job to job. They had probably been driving too fast and, with the great weight of water in the tank, they had managed to overturn the trailer into a ditch thereby losing all the water in the process. They eventually appeared having retrieved the trailer and refilled the tank.

Once we had cleansed we moved on about half a mile to a big lambing shed where the second flock awaited us. We parked our vehicle on the road and whilst we were making ourselves ready we noticed an adjacent entrance leading to the next farm. We could see the owner, a farmer of advanced years, coming up his drive towards us. We thought he was coming to chat to us about things in general, but as he drew closer we could see the dark look on his face. Closing his farm gate in a very defiant manner he muttered something to the effect that all those present would live to regret what they were doing. Somewhat subdued by this gentleman's observations we completed our work for the day. Of all the farmers that we met he was the only one to blame us personally for the slaughter policy.

The following morning we had to kill a flock of 117 sheep where the vets had already killed a few which had lesions the night before. We then helped to pen about another 100 which were in an adjoining field, amongst which were thirty or so stock rams. The owner of these had a much bigger flock of ewes elsewhere and these rams were the sires for this larger flock. We helped with the examination of the sheep's mouths and helped restrain these big rams for blood testing. Several ulcers were found in their mouths and the vets took the decision to slaughter them.

We then accompanied one vet a few hundred yards down the road to try to kill two sheep and one goat, but when we arrived no-one was at home and, as one cannot enter someone's premises and kill their stock without their knowledge, the attempt was abandoned for that day.

A few days later we were called in to kill some sheep belonging to a young man I mentioned in an earlier chapter who kept stock in various locations. We had two vets with us, a young lady from South Africa and a young lady from Norway, who had examined the sheep the night before and had found some mouth lesions. They were sufficiently concerned to slaughter the affected sheep with barbiturate injection and then wrap them in black plastic bags to contain any possible escape of virus. It was our job to slaughter the remainder of the sheep some two hundred in number. Having completed this we returned to the farm gate with the intention of cleansing ourselves in the usual way. We noticed that the sprayer had been delivered with the necessary citric acid but apparently no personnel to do the job of spraying the carcasses. It is known that citric acid inhibits the progress of the virus and it had been customary for this procedure to take place usually after we had departed. We rang the office to offer our services as it was evident that the sooner this procedure was undertaken the better. We were asked to proceed with this work and, bidding goodbye to the two lady vets, we returned to the scene to carry this out. Surprisingly there appeared to be no contiguous killing and we were told we could stand down. I never heard whether these lesions were confirmed as foot and mouth. As we returned to our hotel driving along narrow lanes, we were descending a hill when a driver coming the other way at great speed managed to wedge himself between the bank and our offside front wheel, both vehicles having braked very hard. Amazingly no damage was done to either vehicle and we went on our way, shaken but uninjured.

The disease was still flourishing in other areas of the country, particularly in Settle in Yorkshire and shortly after this we put together a package comprising bulker lorries, hoisting machinery, water bowsers with pressure cleaning equipment and expanding hurdles all on one trailer to handle numbers of sheep plus the necessary personnel including a man with a dog and of course Sam and I to do the slaughtering. We offered this facility around the country but most areas by then appeared to be fairly well organised and our services were not utilised. Much, much later on, after the disease had come to an end, MAFF, which had in the meantime become DEFRA, expressed an interest in our ability to supply a complete team to deal with on farm slaughter should any future outbreak of foot and mouth, swine fever or any of several other unpleasant diseases waiting in the wings occur.

Chapter 17

Change Again

Towards the end of June, having once again spent sufficient time to become "clean", I returned to working on the Farm Animal Welfare Scheme, which had been going on apace throughout the time I had been away.

My first job, with a fairly early start at 4.30 am, was up to Kington, near Hereford, accompanied by Andy. Andy was a sheep farmer himself and also had an interest in market gardening which took up what little spare time he had left when he wasn't driving stock transporters. Within two or three miles of the farm concerned we had to stop to allow a much smaller cattle lorry to reverse into a farmyard. We got out and spoke to the driver. He told us that the lambs that he would be loading were going for slaughter for human consumption. It was good to see that the rest of the world was trying to carry on through this madness as well as it could. The driver enquired where we were bound and for what purpose, so we told him the name of the farm and the fact that we were collecting stock for the Welfare Scheme. His rejoinder, which echoed the general census of opinion, was that the lunatics had escaped from the asylum and were now running the country. He also observed, whilst noting the size or our lorry and being familiar with our destination, that there was no way in the world that we would gain access to the farm as things stood. We said goodbye and continued on our way.

We were met by our farmer and his son by a small cattle grid, which obviously led to the farm itself. Descending from the lorry and assessing the situation I suggested that we cut off the steel handrails around the side of the grid, the uprights of which were made of 2"x2" angle iron welded to the main base and to a piece of scaffold tube above to form a handrail. In the absence of cutting gear at the farm, a hacksaw was eventually produced and we took it in turns to saw our way through. The cattle grid spanned a, now dry, gravel stream bed which one could imagine during the winter or during any summer storms would be quite a torrent. We gingerly negotiated the mutilated cattle grid and ascended a long sloping driveway to the farm. As we did so I noted while looking around me that some of the small fields on either side were almost wall to wall bracken. This pernicious weed, which is totally useless for anything other than cutting and drying for bedding, will inevitably, when the Government has had its way and has driven all the small farms on the hills out of business, strangle all other vegetation. It is only now kept in check by continual cutting and the grazing of sheep.

On arrival at the farm the farmer's wife immediately made tea for everyone while we went to check the details on the licence against the stock presented. This was some 150 ewes and lambs, which the farmer had already separated and six cows with their calves at foot. All the documentation appeared to be in order, so we loaded quite quickly and then were invited in for a bacon breakfast. The generosity of these hill farmers was without fault.

Returning down the hill with a full load it seemed impossible, even with Andy's great driving ability, to return the way we had come. This must have had something to do with the redistribution of weight on the lorry. Our only course of action seemed to be to drag out the remains of the cattle grid and drive down into the shallow stream bed and out the other side. The farmer, who had accompanied us in his Land Rover to see us safely off the premises, returned to the farm for tractor and chains and dragged the entire structure from its moorings allowing us to negotiate the stream bed with care. Wishing him well, we went on our way.

A few days later I was up at 3.30am to be away from the abattoir at 4.30am. I was with a different driver this time: Nick from Stow-on-the-Wold. Our destination was the Mendip hills in Somerset, an area not far from my home but this was the first time I had visited it in the course of this work. From the information on the licence we were expecting to collect ten cows.

On arrival there appeared to be only four cows, one with a calf, which was suffering from a condition called "joint ill". This condition is the result of a bacterial infection gaining access to the body through the unhealed umbilical cord. The infection, properly known as umbilical cord pyaemia, travels first to the liver and at this stage sometimes proves fatal. If the animal survives the initial onslaught, the condition becomes systemic. The bacteria travel in the blood and set up home in the synovial fluids of the joints causing a pus filled arthritis which becomes visually apparent with a gross enlargement of some of the leg joints and severe disability.

There was also another calf whose mother had been shot the night before by the vet, the reason given being that she was too wild and dangerous to be loaded on the lorry. The disparity between the licensed and actual numbers and category of stock necessitated a phone call from me to the office. It was decided that the dead cow and her live calf, which we would take with us, and the cow with the "joint ill" calf would qualify as breeding cows. The remaining three cows, because the vet had written nothing to indicate that he had examined them for pregnancy, would be valued as cull cows, attracting only about one third of the price of the other two. The dead cow would in due course be collected on another parallel scheme to be transported directly to the incinerator. This was one amongst many times whilst travelling in Wales where I found that stock which was due to travel on the welfare licence had already been dispatched by the local vet who had deemed them, for various reasons, unfit to travel. This proved to me that the vast majority of vets involved with the licensing of this scheme did a good professional job. There were however a few who issued licenses with impunity for animals to travel where some of the consignment were in such poor condition that they could not even stand up and if loaded with other stock were in grave danger of being trampled to death. In such cases the drivers would segregate them if space allowed. If the lorry was full, animals in this condition would sometimes be placed in a large box underneath it which in normal conditions was used to carry straw. There were several times when sickly or very recently born tiny lambs were presented for transportation that I, knowing from experience they were particularly vulnerable to being trampled and after first asking for the farmer's permission, destroyed them with a single blow from something heavy. This quick death was preferable to a slow lingering one on the lorry. Sadly I was not able to take proper weaponry with me on these trips to dispatch the older animals. All this led me to believe that a few vets issued licenses without even viewing the stock concerned. Whether this was due to pressure of work or negligence I do not know. What I do know is, that in forty odd years spent in the meat trade I have never before witnessed cruelty to such an extent as that which occurred under this Scheme. Indeed, in the past, I had prosecuted people for transporting animals in such conditions. Unfortunately in my capacity at this time there was little I could do other than relieve the suffering of a few. Sometimes when returning to the abattoir late at night and knowing the animals would not be killed until the following day, I would collect a captive bolt pistol, kept for the purpose at the security gate, and shoot all those animals which were *in extremis.* It has to be said that there were often some animals which had already been trampled to death.

Returning to the events at the Mendip hill farm, we quickly loaded the remaining animals. During conversation with the farmer he told me that he had already sold 70 cows and calves at a considerable loss to go somewhere up in the Midlands and because the licence to remove our animals had been incorrectly filled out he would not receive the proper value for those.

On the return journey it was still very early in the morning and in several places roe deer could be seen grazing in the fields as we passed.

On arrival back at base the day was still young and, after weighing unloading cleansing and disinfecting, the lorry was reweighed and we were ready to set out on another trip. This time we were going near Aberdare, to a farm where we understood the farmer to have had an accident which made it very difficult for him and his wife to cope with the demands of their young family and their numerous stock. One lorry had already been despatched to pick up 200 odd sheep, a portion of the 700 odd he farmed in total. This farm was split into two sites which were some miles apart. We were going in a small lorry to pick up some cattle from one location, while the next day another lorry was going to the other site to collect some more of the cattle. This was necessary, in spite of waste of time and lorry space, because it was not allowed at the time to go from farm to farm, or one area to another, picking up stock on the way.

We had just crossed the Severn Bridge when we received a phone call from the abattoir office warning us that there had been an accident on the M4 and telling us that it would be advisable, if possible, to leave the motorway to avoid hold ups. Acting on this advice, we left the motorway by the Celtic Manor Hotel, a huge imposing landmark in the area, and headed for Abergavenny, later turning onto the heads of the valleys road. The sky ahead was getting darker and darker until we were surrounded by a malevolent deep purple colour. While ascending an incline the heavens opened and the busy dual carriage way became a riverbed with stones from the banks as big as cricket balls rolling towards us. Also there were fountains of water spewing from the steep banks on the sides and reaching half way across the road in front of us. I was glad that we were high up in the cab of the lorry, because most of the cars around us were pulling over as they could not see to drive. Rarely in my life have I experienced such a deluge, although it would have paled into insignificance compared to the later horrendous storm at Boscastle.

Driving out of the rain we continued to our destination where tea and biscuits were immediately offered by the farmer's wife while we awaited the return of the farmer, his wife having summoned him on his mobile. It turned out that there had been a tractor accident the previous February in which he had sustained a double fracture of his spine, in fact he showed me the bony lumps on his back where the fractures had hopefully now healed. These horrendous injuries were obviously very debilitating but had not stopped this man, as soon as he was able to move and stand and against medical advice, from signing himself out of hospital to go home to assist his wife in the lambing of their 700 ewes. At any time in the early stages of healing an awkward movement could have permanently paralysed him. One can only admire the sheers guts and determination of this man and so many others of his kind. It appears to me that these are the sort of people that Mr Blair and Lord Haskins would like to put out of business because they have the audacity to claim subsidies which are rightfully theirs. It appears to many in the countryside that the Government prefers instead to heap money on projects of questionable benefit to Britain that may appeal to the champagne socialists in the cities.

Returning to the job in hand, we were there to collect nine cows and a bull but the farmer was trying to do a deal with one of his neighbours to save the life of the bull which meant that we only loaded nine beautiful suckler cows of Angus, black Hereford and Charolais type, all in superb condition. We said goodbye to this brave man, wished him well and returned to the abattoir.

Chapter 18

Still More Must Die

Another day, another trip and another 4am start. I was beginning to lose track of day and night, getting up in the middle of the night to go to work and sometimes not returning home until the early hours. This time I was with a new companion: an owner–driver called Roger. We set off for Llantwit Major near Swansea to pick up 24 cows.

Once we had left the main road and were travelling the country lanes one lane looked much like another in the dark. A wrong turn in a car is no big problem, but having to turn around in a huge lorry can be a nightmare. We were feeling our way gently towards our destination when a car came up behind us furiously flashing its lights. We stopped to see what the problem was and the car driver came running up to the cab and told us that he was the person in charge of the cattle we were due to collect. As luck would have it he had just saved us from taking a wrong turn. Allowing him to squeeze past us in a gateway, we followed him to the farm, along the way negotiating yet another very narrow cattle grid at the entrance with only a coat of paint to spare on either side.

Our guide was in fact the farmer's nephew. The farmer himself was very old, suffered from arthritis and was only able to get about on two sticks. When we arrived at the farm he came out to greet us and showed me the licence, which was for 24 breeding cows but with no mention on the form of scanning, internal examination, calf at foot or having been seen running with the bull thereby making the classification of 'breeding cows' appear unfounded. If we were to return to the abattoir without further explanation from the vet the farmer would only be paid cull cow rates.

I explained the situation to the farmer and suggested he should contact his vet before we loaded the cattle. It was not yet quite 7 am and it is often difficult to raise normal people at this hour. However the farmer persisted and eventually contacted his vet to whom I again explained the position. He assured me that he would fax the necessary information back to the abattoir to arrive before we did. Accepting this arrangement we were invited in to have a cup of tea and a cake. The nephew told us that we should feel honoured as no-one was usually invited into the house.

The farmer had been living on his own for many years and was a very private man. We were told that the farm was quite extensive and there were many head of suckler cows and beef cattle, all it would seem now looked after by the nephew, the uncle being too infirm to do very much. The reason we were taking some of these cows was to ease the burden on the nephew who ran a pub in his spare time! He also told us that originally he had only come to help out when the hired man ruptured himself, but was still helping out 20 years later. We then went to view the cattle which were extremely wild and the sight of strangers was enough to have them climbing the walls. Apparently whilst being confined in an open yard the night before one had broken its leg. We were told that later that day a knacker man from Somerset was coming to kill that cow and take it away. It occurred to us that it was an awfully long journey to be undertaken to kill one cow and one would have thought there would have been someone else nearer to do the job.

The 23 cows which we were to take were mixed up with about 10 beef steers. These steers were going to be collected later in the day to go to Nottingham and were actually going for human consumption. The problem we had was to separate the cows from the steers and then to run five or six of the cows at a time up into our lorry to be partitioned off. For those of you who have never dealt with cattle, especially very wild cattle, I will explain our predicament. Once one of the group decides to go in any direction the rest will follow in a bunch usually at great speed. From the large open yard where they were corralled we managed to drive the whole lot into a disused milking parlour and by using some of the gates, which still remained within, we eventually succeeded in parting the steers from the cows. Locking the steers in an adjoining shed, we turned our attention to our 23 cows, which by this time were not only wild, but aggressive as well.

Roger stationed himself out of sight behind a door at the base of the gangplank of the lorry, whilst I, with the aid of the nephew and a hastily constructed swing gate, endeavoured to release just five at a time from the milking parlour back out into the yard and thence up into the lorry, all the time trying not to get killed in the rush. Each time a batch of five entered the lorry Roger would try to slam the partitions shut behind them. Unless he moved very fast they would reach the end of the lorry, find they were in a dead end and come back out again twice as fast as they went in. It was only Roger's skill and speed and his ability to duck and dive from years of playing rugby that enabled us to get the job done relatively unscathed. I did however have a very close call with a red Hereford cow that turned quickly and caught me off guard. Shaking her head and pawing the ground as a precursor to a charge, which would probably have splattered me on the railings, it was only by luck that she felt she was getting left behind by the others and changed her mind about the charge. Had she persisted she had me at a disadvantage and I could have been seriously injured or even killed. I heard later that this same cow would not come out of the holding pen at the abattoir and charged anyone who went into the pen to try to drive her out. In the end she had to be shot with a rifle and dragged out of the pen with a rope. We said our goodbyes and returned to the abattoir without further incident.

The next job was, unusually, in the opposite direction over to Oxfordshire with a change of driver, another Roger, and in a very small lorry as it was only to collect eight cattle. It would have helped if we had been given the correct address, but the name of the farm had been given to us as the name of the road in which it was situated. This caused a certain amount of confusion when asking directions from the local population. At one point I alighted from the lorry and crossed the road to talk to an old man who one would think would know his way around his home village. It turned out that he was stone deaf but, despite this, he was more than willing to give me detailed directions to some hypothetical destination. If we had followed his directions we would have ended up in the next county!

There was only one thing for it and in the end we rang the farmer and asked him to come and find us. He duly did and we followed him back through the village whereupon he turned down a tiny lane between a row of houses which opened out into quite a large complex of farmhouse and buildings. This would have been difficult to find even with the correct details.

The cattle involved were eight beautiful black Hereford steers. They had been about to be sent for slaughter for human consumption when the movement restrictions were introduced in February. So that the animals may achieve their best potential, farmers will often keep them alive almost right up to their sell by date of 30 months. This is the age over which even by one minute bovine animals are deemed to be no longer prime beef but become toxic waste. This rule was introduced with the advent of BSE and determines that no bovine animal over 30 months may, for whatever reason, enter into the food chain but instead must be dealt with under yet another scheme called the OTMS (the over 30 months scheme). During the period of foot and mouth restrictions the OTMS scheme was put on hold and the only outlet available to farmers was through the Farm Animal Welfare Scheme. This particular farmer was highly incensed (and there must have been hundreds of other farmers like him) because, through no fault of his own, his animals had gone overnight from valuable food animals to low value cull animals and, to add insult to injury, he had promptly booked them onto the Welfare Scheme in March and this was now July, so he had had to feed and look after them for all those months for absolutely nothing in the way of compensation. As these animals were confined in a barn and not out to grass this would have amounted to large quantities of hay and concentrate in order to have maintained them in the lovely condition that we found them. He was lucky he only had eight! This story is a typical example of how farmers lost money during the crisis, possibly contrary to the perception of some at the time.

Having loaded them with no problem I went into the farmhouse to complete the paperwork whereupon we got back on the road.

Chapter 19

Intrusion, Callous Disregard and Catch 22

Later that week I teamed up with Tommy when we took a small lorry up to an area near Hereford to carry out the first job of the day which was to pick up two cows and two calves. This was my first trip with Tom who nowadays was only able to drive small lorries as a result of an accident in which he had lost an eye. In the past he had driven big cattle lorries but, when loading cattle one day, an animal had kicked a partition gate into his eye causing damage that had necessitated its removal. This once again serves as a reminder of how dangerous it can be when dealing with very large animals on a daily basis. This was but one of many accidents I have seen and heard of over the years. No amount of health and safety legislation can protect you from these and it is only the experience and expertise of animal hauliers and slaughtermen which prevents more accidents from occurring. It should be borne in mind that these workers, unlike the farmers, are dealing with a new set of animals every day and therefore are unaware of any fractious tendencies.

We arrived at the farm just after 6am and had to rouse the farmer's wife who was totally unaware of our mission. The animals in question were in a barn on her property but did not belong to her, but to a farmer in Builth Wells. They were the residue of a much larger bunch of cattle which had already gone, on the Welfare scheme, to an abattoir in the Midlands. These two cows had not been taken because they were actually calving on the day of collection. The farmer's wife told us that her husband was suffering from cancer and was in hospital at the time of our visit. As a result of his condition he had reduced his stock down to 200 sheep and had let the surplus grazing to the man from Builth Wells. It became clear, after several telephone calls, that although the owner of the cattle was aware of the fact that we were coming to collect them he had made no effort to be present or to inform the farmer's wife, even though he was aware of her situation. Nor had he applied for a veterinary licence to move the stock. Without that we were unable to proceed.

I rang the co-ordinator of the Scheme for that area, a man called Ron who operated out of Worcester but who happened to be close by, and he said he would call in to see what he could do. In the end he had to arrange for a vet to visit and then had to go back to Worcester to fetch the necessary paperwork, all of which delayed us for some five hours. During this time the farmer's wife plied us with cups of tea and contacted a kindly neighbour who came to assist us with the loading and told us stories of foot and mouth outbreaks in the vicinity. He had lost his stock in a contiguous slaughter some weeks previously. He told us that the owner of the cattle had come to the farm earlier when some 70 or 80 cattle had been removed and, having clarified some discrepancies on the eartags and passports, had got in his car and departed without helping to load his animals. It also became clear to us that the farmer and his wife had been forced to buy silage bales and feed the animals out of their own pocket because they could not be removed from the farm earlier with the other cattle. This was one of several instances during these months when I inadvertently came across the knock on effect on human lives of the foot and mouth crisis.

The long delay incurred in the morning put us behind schedule and necessitated ringing the second farmer to advise him that our arrival would be much later than anticipated.

On our second journey we retraced our steps of the morning, branching off this time to Builth Wells. The farm was situated up a long lane with other properties on left and right. We came upon a large duck pond on one side of the track on which was sitting a solitary Khaki Campbell duck, however the disturbance caused by the lorry driving past resulted in this single duck being joined by 50 or 60 others. Knowing these to be a good laying strain of duck I can only imagine that this farmer had a penchant for duck eggs!

At the farm we were greeted by a husband and wife team who told us that they had had no income from the farm for months due to the restrictions, and although we were taking three cows and 100 cull ewes this was not going to bring in a fortune! I don't think that the powers that be in their comfortable offices appreciated the predicament that many farmers found themselves in or, if they did, they didn't seem to care. With no money coming in and their only way of making any money in the future being taken away and slaughtered because they could not afford to feed it, many farmers ended up in a catch 22 situation. The daughter of the family, who very wisely had no intention of going into what remained of the farming industry, arrived, changed her clothes and came out to lend a hand with the loading. During our conversation she told me she had taken a job as a doctor's secretary. Wishing them all well we belatedly returned to the abattoir.

Chapter 20

What Should Farmers Do Now?

The next job was a much bigger one with two very large articulated lorries going to a farm near Risca. As it was apparently difficult to find we had arranged to meet the farmer's wife on a motorway roundabout and to follow her in convoy. She duly arrived in her little white pickup but seemed oblivious to the fact that large lorries can't go as fast as small pickups! Because of this she had to stop now and again for us to catch up. Finally she disappeared down a small road between some houses. We had only gone a hundred yards or so down this lane when it became apparent that further progress was impossible due to the narrow width and overhanging trees. After some time she returned to see what had become of us and we tried to explain to her that the dimensions of the lorries and the accessibility of the lane had nothing whatsoever in common and an alternative plan would have to be devised.

The two drivers left me in charge of the lorries while they went ahead in the pickup to assess the situation. After a while they returned shaking their heads in disbelief. We had been told that there was articulated vehicle access as loads of hay and straw had been delivered in the past. All I can say is that the vehicle concerned could have been no bigger than an articulated milk float! The drivers brought with them the licensing vet, another very nice and practical Robert who had been in private practice on the South coast but was presently working for MAFF. We discussed the best way out of this impasse. I told the vet that the instruction from on high was that animals must not be transhipped from lorry to lorry on the highway. However in this instance there was no alternative and the vet took the decision to overrule the diktat decreed by officials ignorant of the physical situations it was possible to encounter. On other occasions when access had been difficult we had taken a small lorry with us to ferry animals out to the road. Unfortunately, because we had been told in this case the access was not a problem, no such provision had been made, so at this late stage in the proceedings we had to try to locate such a small vehicle somewhere in the vicinity. All this took some time and what had started as a comparatively simple job now descended into chaos.

Eventually we were told that a farmer from the Forest of Dean who owned his own lorry for the haulage of his own animals, but who also undertook some contract work, had been located and was on his way. When he arrived it became a case of repetitive loading and unloading, the intervening distance being about a mile, until all the stock was installed in our big vehicles. This operation attracted the attention of the local residents, some of whom engaged me in conversation. I explained that this was just one of hundreds of such events throughout the country where, to my mind, animals were being needlessly slaughtered on the Farm Animal Welfare Scheme.

The Scheme, by which healthy animals were bought by the government, to be slaughtered and disposed of, was said to be needed because the farms of origin were running low on food and the foot and mouth restrictions meant that the animals could not be moved either to fresh grazing on the same farm or to be sent for slaughter for food or bought and sold in the normal trade of the livestock industry. My question was and is, that if taxpayers' money could be used to compensate farmers for the useless slaughter and disposal of these animals, surely that money could have been better used to purchase and transport foodstuffs from areas unaffected by the disease where there was plenty to these stricken farms to enable them to keep their animals alive. If lorries could be sent to all these farms to pick up their animals then surely deliveries of food could have been made in the same way. Local people were appalled to hear that by tomorrow even the tiny little lambs which we were loading would be dead and buried in a huge landfill site in Wiltshire.

Returning to the farm on the last trip to complete the paperwork and to enjoy a final cup of tea, I realised that the whole episode had taken a staggering seven hours to complete. The farmer said to me "I just don't know what I'm going to do now. There does not seem to be any future for me or my son in this way of life that I love." Scratching my head for some ideas to offer him, I thought of the huge Celtic Manor Hotel, which was not far away. Knowing that many rich people go there to play golf and that many of these might also enjoy driven shooting in season I suggested that he could offer them some such facilities. I had already noticed that a large part of his farm was on a very steep wooded escarpment and maybe, in partnership with his neighbours along the same escarpment, he could encompass an area large enough to run a commercial driven pheasant shoot. He would still be able to keep his farming interests going, albeit on a smaller scale, and he could then produce lambs and probably a few pigs to barbeque for after-shoot meals. He could convert some of his old farm buildings into dining areas and kitchen facilities, not dissimilar to the country restaurant which was subsequently created down in Dorset by Hugh Fearnley-

Whittingstall in his programme "Return to River Cottage", but with the added attraction of a day's shooting as a precursor to a delightful meal. With a little bit of advertising clients could very well be attracted from further afield.

The farmer, somewhat bemused by my imagination running riot, said that if it was such a good idea, perhaps I would like to come and run it for him! Declining his offer, but wishing him good luck, we set off on the return journey.

Chapter 21

Another Friday 13th

Friday 13th of July saw us with two lorries heading through the middle of Wales to Brecon. We were to meet the farmer's son at a roundabout just before Brecon so that he could guide us in to the farm. It was a beautiful early morning driving through the Brecon Beacons. We arrived at our rendezvous and the young farmer met us looking very flushed and sweating profusely. I said to him "Don't tell me – Friday 13th – is there a problem?" Looking a bit sheepish he told me that while corralling the relevant cattle five had made their escape and disappeared over the next hill mixing with other cattle as they went.

The plan had been to collect 19 in-calf heifers at one holding and eight suckler cows at another site under the same ownership. We arrived at the first site and found two young men waiting to assist us with the loading. It would appear that they and the farmer's son had been vainly trying to recapture the five escapees and in the process had become very hot and bothered. Together we loaded the remaining heifers, which were extremely wild, and, leaving Nick, one of the drivers, to see if anything could be done about the five escapees, I continued to the second site with Royston the other driver to collect the eight cows. This would not normally have been a problem but, it being Friday 13th and the first part of our mission having gone wrong, I fully expected there to be more difficulties. Sure enough seven cows went into the lorry as quiet as lambs but the eighth decided that there was no way she was going to follow. She made it very plain that if we wished to persist her feelings towards us could easily dramatically change. The only thing to do was to unload three of her companions to keep her quiet and then endeavour to reload all four before she realised quite what had happened. After a couple of attempts this plan succeeded and, closing and sealing the lorry, we returned to the first site to see how they were getting on.

To our surprise all was well as, by gathering all the cattle from several fields and corralling them, they had managed to separate the five escapees and load them. After sealing and disinfecting the lorry we set off on our return journey.

On our return to the abattoir we found the place was stacked solid with animals awaiting slaughter which was taking place as fast as possible to accommodate all the new arrivals, but even so a large backlog had evidently built up. The holding capacity of this plant was enormous however it was but one of many carrying out this murderous and wasteful scheme. On this morning I watched as load after load after load of ewes and lambs were mechanically shovelled into bulker lorries in the bottoms of which were bags and bags of sawdust to soak up the gallons of blood squeezed from the underlying carcasses by the weight of the bodies above. I also saw the skins ripped from the beautiful little beef calves brought in with their suckler mothers to prove their breeding cow status.

The cost of this waste of potential food that was taking place was brought home to me when that same morning the local co-ordinator of this scheme told me that he had had to go to check a consignment of Brazilian beef which had just been imported. Only recently the Government had seen fit to ban the importation of Argentinian beef for fear of possible foot and mouth contamination and yet they were perfectly at ease allowing beef to be brought in from another vast South American country, where presumably similar risks of disease apply. It would appear that they were also perfectly at ease with destroying and wasting our high quality home produced meat animals. The financial cost to the British taxpayer was enormous. The psychological cost to the people in this already beleaguered industry was incalculable.

The following Sunday saw me heading for Llandridnod Wells to pick up a few cows and calves and 150 odd sheep. As we passed through the town itself I was surprised to see that the buildings were larger and more imposing than I was used to seeing in other towns in the area and I surmised this was because it was a spa town and therefore historically more affluent.

The farm itself was situated on one side of a small valley. On the other bank, amongst the gorse bushes, quantities of rabbits could be seen sitting outside their burrows. On reaching the farm I observed on this to the farmer, and he said I would be welcome at any time in the future to come up and reduce the population. As I have more than sufficient rabbiting in Somerset I declined his kind offer as it would take half a day to get there.

We loaded his stock with no problems and as we did so his two young daughters were photographing the proceedings with their little cameras. The farmer told us he had promised to buy some black and white Jacob sheep to be their very own, but of course he could not do this until the restrictions were lifted. His promise to them was largely to take their mind off the departure of these sheep and was something for them to look forward to in the future. The pity was that for the farmers themselves there was no such promise of better times ahead: small wonder that farmers are leaving the land at an unprecedented rate. Indeed, whereas 50 years ago there were half a million farms in this country now less than half that number still remain. Maybe it is not surprising that on average 50 farm workers are driven to take their own lives in desperation every year.

When we arrived back at the abattoir it was again full to capacity with every pen and alleyway full of stock awaiting slaughter the next day. In several pens I noticed some very high quality Limousin cattle, the sort of animals that one would normally see in the stock pens at agricultural shows. These included two massive bulls, some young bulls and a number of cows with calves at foot. When discussing them the next day with the man who brought them in he described this as the crime of the century and told me that the owners were unable to sell them through the normal pedigree sales because of the current restrictions. Unfortunately their circumstances were such that they had to dispose of the cattle and so they had had to resort to the Welfare Scheme. He also told me that when rounding up these cattle prior to loading one of the bulls had taken exception to him and had chased him out of the field. He felt he had been lucky to escape with his life.

Chapter 22

A Brush With The British Army

There were often problems in being punctual for prearranged collection times because of unforeseen circumstances.

On this particular day there was a collection arranged for 2pm near Sennybridge where we were due to pick up four cattle and 150 ewes and their lambs. In the event, we did not set out until 4pm. The farmer had been contacted to advise him of this delay and had said there would be no problem getting to the entrance to the farm as articulated lorries had been there before. However, the farmstead was some quarter of a mile from the entrance and only a small lorry would be able to negotiate this distance. Therefore we travelled with one large articulated lorry, driven by Andy, and one small one, driven by Howard, in which we planned to ferry the stock out to the road.

The journey was uneventful apart from one thing. Whilst approaching the little town of Crickhowell we could see on our right hand side a large number of cars parked and a lot of people milling about outside a farm entrance. We heard afterwards that this had been a protest to try to stop the slaughter of a Friesian Holstein herd which we had often seen grazing when passing on previous journeys. I knew nothing of the circumstances of this slaughter which involved as I understood it not only this herd but the stock on the whole hillside above. We realised that the protest had not been successful when, a few days later, while passing the same way again, we saw the bulker lorries collecting the recently slaughtered carcasses.

Arriving at the village of Sennybridge our instruction was to take a turning right down a hill at the beginning of the village. This led to a tight left hand bend onto a delightful little arched bridge over the river … Andy stopped the large lorry and walked forward to assess the situation. Several times previously Andy's skilful driving had allowed us to successfully cross similar narrow bridges, but this time the sharp bend leading to the bridge was an additional problem. However, after considering the options, Andy said he would have a go. We had already carried out several shunts back and forth to align the lorry, when a young lad appeared on his bike from the other side of the bridge. Dismounting and sitting on the parapet of the bridge he observed, obviously from previous experience, that there was no way we would get that lorry across that bridge. This challenge spurred Andy on to greater endeavour.

After many more shunts, each reverse having to push the lorry up a steep slope, Andy had to admit defeat, much to the amusement of the young man sitting on the wall. The constant revving of the engine had by this time attracted a small crowd of people who had appeared from the neighbouring houses to protect their lovely little bridge. At this juncture I made a phone call to the farmer who suggested that we should withdraw from this access road and continue on through the village until we arrived at the gate of a big Army camp on the right hand side. He said that the Army would be amenable to us going through their camp and thereby crossing the river on a much larger and more substantial bridge.

We duly pulled into the first security gate and I dismounted to seek permission to proceed further through the camp and beyond. Sadly, the officious 'jobsworth' that I encountered announced apoplectically that there was no way that we could continue and that we would have to turn back onto the main road. After allowing him to exercise his little bit of power, I explained to him in simple terms that we were on Government business that had to be completed before the required movement licence expired at 8pm that night. He then took the view that perhaps this was rather more than he could deal with and indicated that I should seek permission from a more substantial security complex 500 yards further into the camp. He would pass the matter on to them by ringing ahead to alert them to our arrival. At this next security post I entered a building to repeat my request yet again, clutching the single piece of paper that showed the details of the farm and the numbers of stock to be picked up. This was all I had in the way of documentation to back up my story until I picked up the licence at the farm.

This time there were two security personnel who told me they would have to seek higher authority. I asked if I could speak to whoever was in charge of the camp but was told that he was in America. I could see that these guys were going to have a bit of fun at my expense. I then enquired who was in charge on the day and this apparently was Major ------- who could be contacted on his mobile phone. I suggested that they did just that and I was then kept waiting for some time while they made a couple of unsuccessful attempts which only achieved the answer phone. At this point, somewhat exasperated, I pointed out to them that time was ticking on and soon the licence would expire in which case we would have to return empty handed, and asked them if they wished to take responsibility for this, or were they prepared to take their courage in both hands and sanction my request. At this, their whole demeanour changed and, after a hurried discussion, they invited me to proceed and said they would provide a motorcycle escort to a gate at the far side of the camp which would return us onto the road we would have been on had we been able to cross the bridge in the village. It was then not far to the farm. They also asked me to ring the number they gave me twenty minutes before we would be due to arrive back at the camp on our return journey.

At last arriving at the farm we found our problems were not yet over. Whereas the ewes and lambs were in order, the four cattle had been described on the licence as four breeding cows but no additional evidence had been given by the vet. This meant a phone call to the vet to explain the possible implications of this omission. He said he would come out to the farm and perform an internal examination of each of these cows, all of whom fortunately turned out to be pregnant. This inevitably caused us further delay, made more pleasant by tea and welsh cakes freely offered by these very hospitable people.

When we were ready to leave I rang the Army number to prepare them for our return and we were again escorted through the camp by motorbike. As we passed between the Army huts we were viewed with some suspicion by the young soldiers, who came out to watch us go by. By this time the two drivers were extremely hungry, this being their second load of the day with little in the way of solid sustenance in between. While the large lorry waited in a lay-by, Howard volunteered to drive the small lorry into the next village where he bought some fish and chips which we all enjoyed immensely.

Feeling much better after our meal we returned to the abattoir and I finally arrived home at about 2am.

Chapter 23

Why Don't We Just Kill All The Sheep?

A few days later we had another 4am start, this time to collect 1000 ewes and lambs from a little village between Cardiff and Bridgend.

We set off in convoy with three large four deck sheep lorries driven by Desi, Ginger and Dai, accompanied by another observer who was a Gloucestershire farmer's wife. She came with us so that one lorry could be loaded first and then return immediately as on this particular day the stock in the lairage was quite low, and once killing commences it is preferred to kill continuously rather than waiting for stock to arrive.

As we neared the farm we passed a secure-looking complex of buildings and chimneys which I was told is where all the old bank notes are incinerated. When we arrived we found that the sheep were confined in a lovely large old building adjoining the farmhouse. It had been, so we were told, an old coach house and the harness hooks and places for storing the horses' collars and tack could still be seen. It had obviously been used for sheep for many years but, with a bit of imagination and restoration, it could have been made into a very attractive dwelling.

The farmer told me that he farmed about 8000 sheep and they were of a variety known as Welsh Mountain Nelson type with a characteristic dark red mane around their necks. These sheep were of high quality and he produced pedigree rams for sale. His disposal of some of his sheep on the Scheme was due in part to a new problem which was the impossibility of getting them shorn. Seasonally gangs of shearers travel from farm to farm, some coming from as far away as New Zealand and Australia, working on a contract basis. The foot and mouth restrictions had affected the free movement of these men and this particular farm being in a 'clean' area had been unable to be visited by shearers who had inadvertently got themselves potentially 'dirty'. The shearing should have been done at least a month earlier and, with the wet and humid weather we had been having, fly strike was rife. The habit of the disgusting little green bottle fly is to lay its eggs in the sheep's fleece, usually under excrement which may be adhering to it, where it is nice and warm and damp. On hatching the maggots burrow through the sheep's skin, feasting on the living flesh beneath and giving off an offensive rotting odour as they do so. This in turn attracts other flies from as far as two miles away who also lay their eggs in the vicinity. On hatching, these maggots will also join in the feast and the sheep, if it is left unattended, will be eaten alive. Under humid wet weather conditions, such as we had been experiencing, the fleece is unable to properly dry out after rain. Then the flies do not restrict their attention to areas of faecal contamination but will indiscriminately lay all over the fleece, resulting in thousands of maggots burrowing into the skin all over the body. The resultant irritation causes so much stress and trauma to the sheep that it will die long before it is eaten alive. If on the other hand the fleece has been removed the short wool dries out quickly and does not attract the fly in the same way. Young lambs can still be vulnerable but as their wool is much shorter it is usually only a problem if the lamb has had diarrhoea and contaminated its back end.

The farmer had already lost many ewes and some lambs and despite the vet treating them with steroids to relieve the itching he was still losing some on a daily basis. I asked him why he had not put more of his stock onto the Scheme while he had the chance. He said that his vet had encouraged him to do so but that he felt that as his were pedigree animals he should try to retain and look after as many as possible. He was trying to maintain some optimism in the midst of his predicament and his aim was to help restock other people when the emergency had died down.

We set about loading 200 odd ewes on to the first lorry which then departed. We then proceeded to load one lorry with all lambs and the other with mostly ewes and a few lambs. There was in fact no need to have brought three lorries as we were only using the lower two decks of each lorry and we could have accommodated 1000 sheep on two lorries.

On our return to the abattoir we found that the ewes on the first lorry had already been slaughtered and were probably by now under the ground in Wiltshire. While we were unloading another lorry came in full of Friesian Holstein heifers. These animals were in perfect condition and just about to calve and start their working lives. Instead, they were to be cut down and burnt. Sadly I learnt that on the farm in Gloucestershire where they came from the farmer had developed multiple sclerosis and had become unable to look after them. As they could not be sold in the normal way they had been put on the Scheme.

The next day was obviously going to be a busy one as lots of us had been allotted a 4am start. My trip was to a farm near Caerphilly, driving again with Andy, to collect 50 ewes and lambs of the Welsh mountain type. This farmer had wanted to dispose of 100 ewes but had been told he could only send 50. At about this time my farming neighbour at home applied to send some cull cows on the Scheme and was turned down flat. This appeared to indicate a change of policy as until now the impression we had was that the powers that be wished to kill as much as possible, particularly to reduce the national flock. Now it seemed money must be getting short and restrictions on numbers were brought in. We were in little doubt that the politicians would dream up some other crazy project to squander taxpayers' money on.

As things turned out the catastrophe of 9/11 was just around the corner leading to an unbelievably sudden end to the foot and mouth debacle. Before long we would be sending our young men to die rather than farm animals while prosecuting two wars at enormous expense to the public purse. While conducting the so called "War on Terror" the death, destruction and misery caused to decent Afghan and Iraqi people seemed to be of no consequence to our politicians who at the same time cosseted the potential perpetrators of terrorist obscenities lurking amongst us.

Returning to the job in hand the road took us over yet another narrow bridge but by this time Andy had become an expert in negotiating narrow bridges. On either side of us were some delightful properties in what was obviously a fairly affluent area. We now found that my mobile had no signal and Andy had left his in another lorry so we were unable to make our usual call ahead to pinpoint the exact location of the farm. As we continued up a hill and down the other side we were now approaching Caerphilly itself and we could see that every gateway and available space was full of rubbish. It seemed that the town's despicable fly tippers had driven a little way into the country to deposit their waste. They obviously considered the rural area outside their town to be of no more value than a rubbish tip. The contrast between this squalor and the delightful surroundings on the other side of the hill was most marked.

Trying my mobile again I was able to contact the farmer who commented that he had seen us go past some time before! Retracing our steps we took the appropriate turning and crossed yet another little bridge under some low trees before reaching the farm. The father and son that we met were obviously put out at having their quota of sheep reduced and whereas the father was perfectly civil, the son was miserable to the point of being unpleasant and appeared to hold us personally responsible for the number reduction. A cup of tea was obviously out of the question and when we wished them goodbye he could barely be bothered to grunt in reply. This behaviour was in direct contrast to the hospitality we normally enjoyed.

Chapter 24

Complications

Sunday afternoon saw me heading down the M4 for the Merthyr Tydfil junction and then branching off up into the hills in the direction of Sennybridge. As we drove through the hills we could see that sheep holding pens were being constructed in places at some distance from the road and we noticed that areas, which were to be used to blood test the sheep on those hills, had been covered with red tarpaulins. We could also see the beginning of the roundup, with long white lines of sheep, driven on by collie dogs and Land Rovers, streaming down the hillsides. I commented to Nick the driver "I'll bet those sheep never return to the hills after their blood has been tested". My thoughts then returned to a conversation I had had some months ago with a friend in the Ministry who predicted the demise of all the sheep on the Brecon Beacons. Sadly I won my bet. I heard later that the sheep we saw that day had all been slaughtered in the newly erected pens, and my friend's prediction became partly true as indeed some thousands of Beacon sheep were eventually slaughtered. I now cannot help wondering, if the sheep were such a risk, why we were allowed to haul stock from this potentially contaminated area to other parts of the country? I also later found myself remembering conversations I had with various hill farmers who said that two or three years previously they had been visited by an official wishing to know the numbers of their sheep which led to them being told they must reduce their flocks dramatically. They then heard no more until the outbreak of foot and mouth disease.

We had taken just a small lorry to collect two cows. As they were booked in as breeding cows and there was no mention of calves at foot, the precaution had been taken of ringing the farmer and explaining to him the criteria necessary to prove breeding cow status, and that this must be apparent on the licence issued by his vet. Thinking that all was well, we arrived near the farm only to find that even a small lorry could not negotiate the tiny lane to the farmstead. The farmer said he would bring the two cows down to the road in a horsebox and there seemed no alternative but to agree to this. The transfer was easily completed and I sealed the lorry. On examining the licence the farmer gave me I found, to my dismay, that the proof offered for the cows' breeding status was that the farmer had said the cows were running with the bull. I told him that this was not good enough and that it must be the vet himself who states he has seen the bull with the cows. I therefore returned to the house with the farmer to phone the vet, leaving Nick in charge of the lorry. I spoke to the vet who said that the woman who had written out the licence had not realised the full implications, and that he had indeed seen these cows running with the bull. I asked him to fax this information immediately to the abattoir to ensure the farmer would get his money. While all this was going on the farmer's father and mother were both in the farm kitchen and whereas mother happily chatted away to me, father, after the initial greeting never said a word. I don't think this was due to rudeness, just that he was shy of strangers, not surprising considering the isolation of his lifestyle. I drank a cup of tea with them and tea was also put in a flask to take down to Nick. When this had been drunk we departed.

Taking a slightly different route on our return journey, the road climbed steeply up a hill with open moorland and sheep watching us on either side. What magnificent views were to be seen in every direction on this beautiful summer morning! One does not need to go on holiday to exotic climes when such scenery is available in our own country.

Chapter 25

Comparisons

Another day and I was travelling for the first time with Louise who was helping out her father, Howard, with whom I had driven many miles. Louise was a very accomplished young lady who was not only qualified to drive large lorries but was much travelled and was presently studying for a degree. On this day we were taking a very small lorry to collect four sows not far from Caerphilly. We did not think we would be very long as it was not very far to go. How wrong we were!

Nearing our destination we rang the farm and were given very vague directions by a woman who we took to be the farmer's wife. We found a tiny lane which had more the appearance of a dry stream bed than a road and which wound its way up a steep hill. At the top this lane levelled out onto something of a plateau and a farmhouse and range of buildings came into view. As we approached the buildings the lane became littered on both sides with piles of builders waste, old fridges, dead cars, stacks of old galvanised sheets and various other heaps of debris which completed a picture of an impoverished and generally run down establishment. This was in dramatic contrast to the vast majority of other holdings that I visited which, although there may have been a shortage of cash, were usually well maintained. A woman emerged from the house, still in her dressing gown with a towel around her head having evidently just come from her bathroom. I asked her where the farmer might be found and, after responding that she didn't know, she disappeared behind the house to look for him. While she was gone I looked into a large galvanised building from which a cacophony of pig squealing was emanating. In a small area at one end, on a bed of dried compacted faeces several feet thick, were penned some thirty or forty young pigs. Not a shred of bedding was in evidence and, judging by the state of them, their allocation of food was minimal. At the other end of the building were four very thin sows - one to the point of emaciation with open sores on its spine. When they became aware of my presence they worked themselves up into a frenzy of anticipation at the possibility of receiving something to eat. It crossed my mind that for any animals we might remove from this establishment for slaughter it would be a happy release. Just then the woman returned, saying that she could not find the farmer and the best thing I could do was to wander around until I came across him. She then went back into the house and showed no further interest in the proceedings.

I could see a stationary tractor and trailer on a track some way further up the hill so I set off in that direction. As I drew near I could see that the trailer was fully loaded with soil and rubble, obviously the result of some excavation somewhere, and was on its way to deposit this load further up the hill. One of the tractor wheels had got a puncture and the whole lot had just been left in the track way and had been there for sometime as weeds were growing amongst the rubbish. Skirting around this obstacle I continued on up the hill for about half a mile amongst sheep and ponies until I spotted a figure on a quad bike a further half mile on, driving amongst some sheep with a collie dog running behind. I started to wave my arms about to attract attention which I eventually achieved as he gave me an acknowledging wave. I assumed he would come down to see what I wanted but he just carried on with what he was doing. I decided to sit down and await developments. As I looked down into the valley deep below me I could see the village which we had passed through on our way here. I had been struck by the poverty-stricken air of the place. Several of the houses and shops were boarded up and rubbish was lying about in the streets.

After about half an hour the farmer decided to descend the hill to see what I wanted. As he approached I could see something white draped across the front of the quad bike and, as he drew nearer, I could see it was the carcase of a sheep. As he came nearer still, I could also smell it since it was in a state of advanced decomposition, shedding maggots and pieces of rotten flesh as he went. "What are you doing here?" he demanded. I explained that I was there to collect some pigs that he had put on the Welfare Scheme. "I didn't know anybody was coming today" he said "and I haven't got a movement licence anyway." I suggested that he should come down to the house with me to sort matters out as we had not made this journey just for fun. He invited me to ride on the back of the quad bike, rather nearer to the decomposing sheep than I would have wished. As we bounced around over the rough ground small pieces of rotten sheep and an occasional maggot went whistling back past me. I would have thought that when an animal had been dead this long it would have been preferable to leave it to sink quietly into the ground rather than trying to carry it around spreading bits everywhere. Shortly after I boarded the quad bike behind the farmer it decided to give up the ghost. The farmer commented that it was always doing this. As we were still on a fairly steep gradient we free-wheeled a further few hundred yards until the ground rose slightly in front of us causing the bike to come gently to a halt. We dismounted and continued the rest of the way on foot.

While we were walking the farmer said that he had booked in 60 odd pigs and several hundred sheep on the Welfare Scheme, however our instruction was to collect only four sows. I had no idea of the reasons for this disparity. I suggested he rang his vet to explain the urgency of the situation and to ask him to come out and issue the necessary licence. He disappeared into the house with no offer of a cup of tea, which was probably just as well because if the inside of the house was as bad as the outside the inclination would have been to decline. While he was gone we had the opportunity to assess the place still further and I noticed that outside the back door were two brand new rabbit hutches. Knowing how much one has to pay for such items, particularly if purchased at a garden centre, it struck me as a strange use of resources when livestock was suffering from lack of food and rabbit hutches could easily have been made from the abundance of demolition material which littered the premises.

Eventually the farmer returned to say that the vet would be with us within the hour, but that the visit would necessitate the viewing of all the stock on the farm prior to granting the licence. By now we realised we were in for a long haul. The vet, in the shape of a young lady, arrived quite quickly and went about the stock viewing in a businesslike manner. Having looked at all the pigs around the buildings she then had to go up onto the hill to view the sheep. The farmer said that by now the quad bike would probably have recovered from its exertions of the morning and he suggested that the vet should walk with him up the hill to where we had left it and, were he to be successful in goading it into action, they could then proceed on the bike. I called the vet to one side as she was setting off and suggested that she tucked herself well in behind the farmer to try to avoid being splattered by odd pieces of decaying sheep flesh and flying maggots. She looked fairly horrified at my suggestion and I think at that stage she thought I was joking. When she eventually returned after a further hour I could tell by the look on her face that she had found to her cost that I hadn't been! We then found that she didn't have the necessary paperwork with her, which meant that she had to return to the surgery. She knew that we had been hanging around for the best part of the day and suggested that she would meet us on the junction of the M4 to hand over the licence. We then loaded the four sows, curiously the one with the open sores on its back was not one of them so unfortunately we had to leave this poor devil and all the others to their fate in this pig Belsen. As we drove away we reflected on some men's inhumanity to animals and also on the fact that a job that should have been very quick had taken nearly six hours. Our rendez-vous with the vet completed, we started on our return trip.

My experiences on the very next day, when I went with Royston to Cwmbran to collect eight bulls, were a total contrast. Initially we had some difficulty in finding the place because it was up a very long lane but when we arrived I met one of the most interesting farmers I had thus far encountered. Whereas I was expecting to see eight barley beef bulls I was in fact shown eight pedigree Aberdeen Angus. In happier times these animals would have been destined for the pedigree bull sales at Perth in Scotland. However, because they could not be transported to any other farm to carry out their function in life, which was to produce thousands of little Aberdeen Angus calves, they were destined to be wastefully slaughtered, following which several tonnes of rippling muscle and flesh beneath their shining black hides would be burnt like so much rubbish. What a crazy world we live in!

This farmer loved his animals and took great pride in striving for perfection in the breed he had chosen. His bearded face and rugged features had seen much in his many years of farming, but his dismay at the current political indifference towards the demise of the small farmer in this country was very evident. He told me that as a young boy of twelve or so he would return from school to his father's holding in mid Wales and would be expected to take a cart horse with some chains and an axe and a spade and dig up and drag out one or more of the many scrub thorn trees growing on the hill. On another day he would be expected to cut down and burn an area of bracken growing higher than he was - all this to turn the land into productive sheep pasture. His father, who had been a miner previously, had been granted the tenancy of his hill farm free of charge on the understanding that he would improve the land. After some years and much hard work the family were given notice to quit the land and offered the tenancy of another unimproved farm so that the first holding could be let to a paying tenant, which goes to show that even back then small tenant farmers had a hard time of it!

It would seem that even this grinding hard work had not put him off the agricultural life and, in spite of his impoverished early days, he now had his own holding and had become well known locally and nationally for his speciality of breeding Angus bulls. Listening to his fascinating stories of yesteryear made me completely forget the reason for me being on his farm and I managed to leave the passports for the eight bulls on his kitchen table. Realising my mistake a little way into the return journey I rang him and he promised faithfully that he would put them into the post first class so they should arrive the next day when the bulls were due to be slaughtered.

Another interesting character I met in the course of this work was David Handley, a farmer of Jersey cattle, who figured prominently in the Farmers For Action organisation which was formed to protest at the low prices paid to farmers for their produce (particularly milk); the proliferation of cheap food imports and the high cost of fuel. I went to his farm on the day that many readers may well remember when the then deputy Prime Minister took a swing at a protesting farm worker while visiting Rhyl in North Wales. Mr Handley told me that he would have been at the same protest over fuel prices were it not for my visit to remove cattle from his premises. I found him to be a brave and highly principled man. Although there are probably many more men out there of his calibre in despair about what is happening to the small farm community in this country, few are prepared to put their heads above the parapet as he and his associates were willing to do, possibly at ongoing cost to their personal lives and future privacy.

Conclusion

In the proceeding chapters I have described a small part of my personal experiences during the time of the foot and mouth crisis of 2001. Although it was a national crisis and most of the population would have been fully aware of it through newspaper and television coverage, with dramatic scenes of grotesquely bloated bodies on funeral pyres, nevertheless relatively few people were directly involved or affected by it. The events of those days, however mismanaged, however horrific and however traumatic for those involved, now pale into comparative insignificance because the world has turned again and now people, instead of animals, are being slaughtered. Unless you happen to be a relative or friend of those tragically murdered, in which case you would never forget, these events soon fade in the public memory. Similarly with the foot and mouth crisis: those involved will never forget, but to vast numbers of the population it is only a distant memory. I feel strongly that it is important to record the events of 2001 from the point of view of someone actually involved in the day to day enforcement of the Government's Schemes. Albeit unintentionally, these Schemes and the movement restrictions brought about animal suffering on a vast scale: an instance of bureaucracy gone mad preventing farmers from even moving stock across a road to fresh pasture. This caused animals to starve where alternative feed was not available; lambs and calves to be born into a quagmire of mud from which they never rose; and sheep to be eaten alive by maggots because the shearing gangs were not permitted to reach them.

There were also shortcomings in the transportation system. There were many delays in the collection of animals in extremis and, as I have already mentioned, many occasions when animals totally unfit for travel had to be loaded, often with dire results.

Doubt has been cast on the origin of the initial infection. Many believe the disease was well established in sheep in the north of England for some time before February 2001. Officially, however, the sows from Heddon-on-the-Wall were the first to be diagnosed and blame for their infection, without any confirmation, was laid at the door of Chinese restaurants in the area. When the symptoms were found in the sows the Government took the decision to wait for the blood test results before banning livestock movements. It took three days for the results to come through. This delay proved to be disastrous as during this time many thousands of animal movements took place, some from one end of the country to the other, a fact of which the Ministry later claimed to be unaware. It resulted in many potentially infectious animals being moved around the country and probably exacerbated the situation. Since those days traceability of animals in this country has been tightened up to the point of strangulation. In contrast, partly as a result of Customs and Excise staff being overstretched, it seems not enough is done to stop the illegal importation of meat. Publicity has been given to the seizures of some consignments, and we have seen on the television pictures of burnt, semi-mummified and in some cases stinking carcasses of rats, monkeys and lizards. It would seem that these are preferable, but expensive alternatives to our hygienically and ethically home-produced animal products for some of our fellow citizens. In view of the fact that a burnt and mummified rat might fetch as much as £17, one may venture to suggest that perhaps our beleaguered sheep, pork and beef farmers, having been told by Lord Haskins to diversify, may turn their attention to the lucrative production of rats!

Perhaps less publicity has been given to the potential health hazards of such a trade. The carcasses may well be carrying a variety of animal diseases which could be transmitted to our own livestock. In addition they may carry zoonotic diseases which are those which have the ability to transmit from animal to man, for example the deadly Ebola virus in the case of monkeys, Weils disease in the case of rats and various *Salmonellas* in reptiles, to name but a few. And then of course there is the ever-present risk of the *Clostridium botulinum* organism proliferating in the foetid and anaerobic conditions to be found within a sealed plastic bag. *Botulism* is without doubt a potential killer of those who eat infected products.

When draconian restriction measures were introduced clearly no thought had been given to the knock on effects on rural industries, particularly the tourist and recreational industries. When the Government realised that the tourist industry was worth far more to the country than agriculture they back pedalled furiously. Initially footpaths in suburbia where no farm animals had trod for years had been needlessly closed, then suddenly fell walking, where foot and mouth was rampant, was opened up again to the few tourists who had not already been frightened off by the pictures of burning bodies on the television. The buzz word at the time was "bio-security". The meaning of this varied from cleansing cabinets for vehicles with spray jets at all angles to other places where a bucket of disinfectant was available and, if you were lucky, a brush to go with it. When it came to cleansing the farms which had been slaughtered out, vast sums of taxpayers' money were squandered on ridiculous measures such as the removal and replacement of concrete yards because they might have been cracked. Had these people never considered that just a few feet away from these yards would be hedges and fields which it would be impossible to pressure clean and sterilise?

At first the bodies of slaughtered animals were contained and burnt on the farms of origin. Later on, when it was considered that the pollution from the pyres was unacceptable, it was suddenly deemed to be perfectly safe to transport infected bodies, some in a state of advanced decomposition where they had been left lying many days before collection, across miles of countryside, often through uninfected areas, to an incinerator. Similarly live animals on the Welfare Scheme were sometimes taken from farms almost adjoining areas where foot and mouth slaughter was taking place and again transported through miles of countryside to their point of slaughter. The resultant carcasses were then taken over vast distances either to land fill or to incineration. All this, while farmers could not move their starving sheep into the next field! Surely if these animals were going to be moved anyway, they could have been taken to an abattoir for human consumption? Surely food could have been transported to those animals that needed it? It makes one wonder whether the whole sorry debacle was part of a bigger plan. I have often pondered on the sheer numbers of animals, particularly sheep, killed at this time and, although I am a supporter of the slaughter policy and contiguous cull for both foot and mouth and swine fever outbreaks, I felt at the time, and still do, that the outbreak was used as an excuse to reduce the national flock. I also believe that the slaughter would have continued for longer had it not been for 9/11, after which event the outbreak came to a remarkably sudden end and political priority focused instead on the "War

On Terror". Indeed, who knows whether the initial infection was not terrorist induced. It would have been easy to obtain infectious material from one of the many countries where the disease is endemic and rub it on the nose of some poor unsuspecting sheep!

Post script

Coincidentally, just at the time that this book was going to press it would appear that research has been done (by the University of Lancaster) which has revealed that many farmers and others involved in this tragic event exhibited symptoms of deep distress for many months. Furthermore, it seems this effect is not confined to this country alone, but has been recognised in other countries, in particular Holland, where the outbreak was minimal by comparison to the debacle in Great Britain.

On a personal note, I have recently revisited several of the sites where we operated. At one particular farm, which had been re-stocked, I was welcomed in, and had a long chat with the farmer and his wife over a cup of tea. He told me that two of his neighbours whose stock we had also slaughtered had been so traumatised by the event that they had not returned to livestock farming, so the result of the tragedy in these cases has been to affect the course of the rest of their lives. If this effect has been replicated over the whole of the country there must be hundreds of farmers who are to this day devastated by the events of 2001.

Also, at the time of writing we hear of the imminent threat of an avian flu outbreak with all its possible implications for human health, and again a catastrophic financial effect for individual farmers.

But at the end of the day, does any of this really matter? With the political emphasis on the importation of all our food our farmers are surplus to requirements but I wonder what will happen when the crunch really comes and we need them to feed us again!